Series

Work Out

Graphic Communication

GCSE

The titles in this series

For examinations at 16+

Accounting
Biology
Chemistry
Computer Studies
Economics
English
French
German
Graphic Communication

Human Biology
Mathematics
Numeracy
Physics
Social and Economic History
Sociology
Spanish
Statistics

For examinations at 'A' Level

Accounting
Applied Mathematics
Biology
Chemistry

English Literature
Physics
Pure Mathematics
Statistics

For examination at college level

Dynamics
Electromagnetic Fields
Electronics
Elements of Banking
Engineering Thermodynamics

Fluid Mechanics
Mathematics for Economists
Operational Research
Organic Chemistry
Waves and Optics

MACMILLAN
WORK OUT
SERIES

Work Out

Graphic Communication

GCSE

A. Yarwood

MACMILLAN
EDUCATION

First published 1988

Published by
MACMILLAN EDUCATION LTD
Houndmills, Basingstoke, Hampshire RG21 2XS
and London
Companies and representatives
throughout the world

Printed in Great Britain by Bath Press, Avon

British Library Cataloguing in Publication Data
Yarwood, A. (Alfred), *1917–*
Work out graphic communication GCSE.—
(Macmillan work out series).
1. Graphic communication — For schools
I. Title
001.56
ISBN 0–333–46537–7

Contents

Preface

This book has been written to help pupils and students to study, learn and revise for GCSE examinations in the subjects of Graphic Communication and Technical Communication. Its contents are based on the syllabuses for GCSE Graphic Communication and Technical Communication as published by the five GCSE examination groups. Each chapter takes a topic from the syllabuses, and after describing the methods by which each topic is developed, goes on to give complete answers to questions such as those which will be set in examination papers. Further questions, many taken from GCSE examination papers, are then set as exercise material for the reader. The final chapter in the book contains answers to the exercises set in each chapter.

Two topics from the syllabuses which have been given prominence here are design and project work. All the CDT subjects — Craft, Design and Technology (CDT) — are linked by the common theme of designing. Graphic Communication is no exception. Although only one chapter is completely devoted to both this topic and how to answer examination questions related to it, the theme of design runs through the whole book. Without Graphic Communication to note, develop and communicate design ideas, CDT designing could not proceed very far. In addition, particular attention has been given to design in project work. The longest chapter is given over to specimen Graphic Communication projects, and how to prepare and present them for moderation in the examination. In this subject, the GCSE examination groups are awarding 30–40% of the total marks in the examination for projects developed by pupils and students during the final two terms of their courses and presented for marking by moderators appointed by the examination groups.

Those learning the subject soon realise the importance of developing good graphic skills. No matter how well the subject is learned, there remains the need to practise drawing, both with and without instruments, in order to be able to produce good quality graphic work. The student sitting for examinations in this subject would be well advised to try to make sure his or her drawing skills are good. It is only through practice that drawing skills can be fully developed. With this in mind, the reader is advised to work through and to draw as many of the specimen answers as time permits, and to attempt to answer all the exercise material — preferably before looking at the answers in the final chapter. Some 10% of the total marks for the examination will be awarded for evidence of good graphic skills.

Each chapter ends with a series of notes entitled *Have You Observed the Following Drawing Procedures?* These are given partly for revision of the contents of each chapter, but also as tips to follow when producing answers to examination questions.

May I finish by wishing you good luck and every success in obtaining a good grade in your examination.

Salisbury, 1988   A. Y.

Acknowledgements

The author and publishers wish to thank the following who have kindly given permission for the use of copyright material:

The London and East Anglian Examining Group for GCSE Examinations; The London Regional Examining Board; The Southern Regional Examining Board; The Welsh Joint Education Committee; The Southern Examining Group; and The Scottish Examinations Board for questions from past examination papers and from specimen GCSE examination papers.

The above-mentioned examination group and boards accept no responsibility whatsoever for the accuracy or method in the answers given in this book to actual questions set by them. The answers given throughout this book are solely the responsibility of the author.

Organisations Responsible for GCSE Examinations

In the United Kingdom, examinations are administered by the following organisations. Syllabuses and examination papers can be ordered from the addresses given here:

Northern Examining Association (NEA)

Joint Matriculation Board (JMB)
Publications available from:
John Sherratt & Sons Ltd
78 Park Road
Altrincham
Cheshire WA14 5QQ

North Regional Examinations Board
Wheatfield Road
Westerhope
Newcastle upon Tyne NE5 5JZ

Yorkshire and Humberside Regional Examinations Board (YREB)
Scarsdale House
136 Derbyside Lane
Sheffield S8 8SE

Associated Lancashire Schools Examining Board
12 Harter Street
Manchester M1 6HL

**North West Regional Examinations
   Board** (NWREB)
Orbit House
Albert Street
Eccles
Manchester M30 0WL

Midland Examining Group (MEG)

**University of Cambridge Local
   Examinations Syndicate** (UCLES)
Syndicate Buildings
Hills Road
Cambridge CB1 2EU

**Oxford and Cambridge Schools
   Examination Board** (O & C)
10 Trumpington Street
Cambridge CB2 1QB

Southern Universities' Joint Board
   (SUJB)
Cotham Road
Bristol BS6 6DD

**East Midland Regional
   Examinations Board** (EMREB)
Robins Wood House
Robins Wood Road
Aspley
Nottingham NG8 3NR

**West Midlands Examinations
   Board** (WMEB)
Norfolk House
Smallbrook
Queensway
Birmingham B5 4NJ

London and East Anglian Group (LEAG)

**University of London School
   Examinations Board** (L)
University of London Publications
   Office
52 Gordon Square
London WC1E 6EE

London Regional Examining Board
   (LREB)
Lyon House
104 Wandsworth High Street
London SW18 4LF

East Anglian Examinations Board
   (EAEB)
The Lindens
Lexden Road
Colchester
Essex CO3 3RL

Southern Examining Group (SEG)

The Associated Examining Board
   (AEB)
Stag Hill House
Guildford
Surrey GU2 5XJ

**University of Oxford Delegacy of
   Local Examinations** (OLE)
Ewert Place
Banbury Road
Summertown
Oxford OX2 7BZ

Southern Regional Examinations Board
  (SREB)
Avondale House
33 Carlton Crescent
Southampton
Hants SO9 4YL

South-East Regional Examinations
  Board (SEREB)
Beloe House
2–10 Mount Ephraim Road
Royal Tunbridge Wells
Kent TN1 1EU

South-Western Examinations Board
  (SWExB)
23–29 Marsh Street
Bristol BS1 4BP

Scottish Examination Board (SEB)

Publications available from:
Robert Gibson and Sons (Glasgow) Ltd
17 Fitzroy Place
Glasgow G3 7SF

Welsh Joint Education Committee (WJEC)

245 Western Avenue
Cardiff CF5 2YX

Northern Ireland Schools Examinations
  Council (NISEC)

Examinations Office
Beechill House
Beechill Road
Belfast BT8 4RS

1 Introduction

1.1 The Examination

There are a number of similarities in the methods by which Graphic Communication is examined by the five GCSE examining groups. In general the syllabuses cover three areas of study:

1. *Common Core* knowledge and applications;
2. **Either** *Graphic Communication* **or** *Technical Communication* knowledge and applications; ·
3. *Project* work.

(a) Common Core

This covers such elements of graphics as the following:

- *Geometry* — plane and solid geometry;
- *Projections* — orthographic, isometric and cabinet projection and drawing;
- *General* — presentation, graphs and charts, drawing to scale, developments;
- *Equipment and Instruments* — use of drawing equipment, drawing aids.

(b) Graphic Communication

This covers elements such as:

- *Projections* — planometric drawing, one-point estimated perspective drawing, two-point perspective drawing. With the aid of instruments or working freehand.
- *Diagrams* — logograms, pictograms, monograms, ideograms, flow diagrams, electric and electronic circuits, fluidic circuits;
- *Colour* — in a variety of media — colour pencil, water colour, toning;
- *Shading* — shadows, shading to produce 3-D effects.

(c) Technical Communication

This covers elements such as:

- *Engineering Drawing*

or

- *Building Drawing*.

(d) Project

Work carried out during one or two terms of the candidate's last year prior to sitting the examination. The work must be based on a topic or on a theme. Depending upon the examining group, the topic or theme may be selected by the candidate or by his/her teacher or lecturer or chosen from a list issued by the examining group.

1.2 The Form of the Examination

In general the examination consists of two (sometimes three) 'written' papers, the first of which is the Common Core paper and the second a choice between Graphic Communication and Technical Communication, the choice being the candidate's. It should be noted that in the subject Graphic Communication the term 'written' does *not* mean that the answers are written in the normal sense of the word. Answers to examination papers in this subject are always drawn, although occasionally short written answers may be required.

1.3 Weighting of Marking of Examination Papers

Although the weighting of marks varies slightly between the five examining groups, the marking follows the pattern:

- *Common Core* — between 35% and 40% of total marks;
- *Graphic Communication* **or** *Technical Communication* — between 25% and 30% of total marks;
- *Project* — between 30% and 40% of total marks.

1.4 Weighting of Marking within Examination Papers

The weighting of the elements of the marking schemes for the three types of 'paper' varies slightly between the five examining groups. However, there is a similarity, the marking following a pattern such as:

- *Knowledge* — between 25% and 30% of total marks;
- *Graphic Skills* — between 25% and 30% of total marks;
- *Applications* — between 25% and 30% of total marks;
- *Design* — between 15% and 30% of total marks.

(a) Compulsory Questions

Most of the papers set by all examining groups will consist of questions, all of which are **compulsory**. A choice **is** given between answering Graphic Communication papers and Technical Communication papers, but even when that choice has been made, the questions within the chosen paper are generally of a compulsory nature.

'Written' papers include questions of a *structured* type. All candidates should be able to start answering these structured questions, which are designed in such a way that as answering proceeds, they become increasingly more difficult. It is to **every** candidates's advantage **always** to attempt to answer all compulsory questions, because some marks will be given for all partially completed answers to structured questions.

Note 2

Common core papers will include *objective*-type questions. These are usually short-answer questions, often requiring only a letter, a word or a phrase as an answer. Objective-type questions may involve making a choice between possible answers. It is best not to guess the answer, but to go into the examination well prepared by revising all the topics in the syllabus for the examination.

1.5 The Importance of Project Work

Note that the project which all candidates must complete during their last year of study for the examination carries between 30% and 40% of the total marks for the examination. The project work is usually assessed and marked by the candidate's teacher or lecturer and then either sent by post to the examining group's offices, or a moderator visits the school or college to check (moderate) the teacher/lecturer's marking. Moderation is often carried out on a selective basis, but candidates must always assume that the marks awarded by their teacher/lecturer for *their* project will be moderated.

Projects must usually be completed by the end of May in the year in which the examination takes place.

Moderators will expect high standard of graphics in the projects which they are checking, and because of the high percentage of marks available for project work, it is advisable:

1. To choose a project topic which is suited to one's own interests and ideas.
2. To make certain that the project is complete and well produced.
3. To make the best use of the time available and not to leave your work on the project until the last possible moment.

Note:

Four specimen projects are given in Chapter 14, together with information about project work and methods of producing graphic communication projects.

1.6 Design

Note that, depending upon which examining group has set the examination papers for which you entered, the mark for the design element in the examination lies between 15% and 30%. About half of this percentage will be awarded for the design element in your project work. Information about design in Graphic Communication examinations is given in Chapter 12.

1.7 Instruments and Equipment

It is common practice for schools and colleges to have sufficient instruments and equipment available for students who are undertaking a course of study in Graphic Communication. When it comes to sitting the examination papers, such instruments and equipment will also be available. However, it is advisable for those studying the subject to possess and use their own instruments, not only so that they become used to them and so probably produce better work, but also because it enables them to work at home, where school/college equipment is not available. Candidates should possess their own rules, set squares, compasses, pens, pencils and erasers. A set of good-quality pencil crayons is also recommended.

1.8 Drawing Aids

All Graphic Communication syllabuses now recommend the use of drawing aids such as French curves, Flexicurves, radius curves, lettering stencils, ellipse templates, and templates for drawing symbols in circuitry drawings. Practice in the use of such aids greatly improves the quality of graphics, particularly in project work. When sitting for an examination, it is best to take some aids into the examination room. A set of French curves (or a Flexicurve) for assistance in drawing curves, a radius curve for drawing radii and a lettering stencil could prove to be of value. You should also have some colour pencils when sitting the examination papers.

1.9 Cleanliness

Cleanliness of hands, paper and instruments is very important when producing drawings. Hands should be washed before commencing work and instruments should be cleaned on paper towels or with a piece of soft cloth. Be careful when erasing unwanted linework that rubber dust does not accumulate on the paper. It can cause dirty marks from the pencil dust it carries.

1.10 Technique

The practice of good graphic techniques makes a great deal of difference between good and bad drawing and will always result in a better mark rather than a poorer one in an examination. You should pay close attention to details such as: layouts of drawings; good linework that is sharp and with a clear difference between outlines lines, construction lines and those lines which should be thin lines; good clear lettering and figures; good dimensioning; well-applied colour work; the accurate use of the British Standards Institution's (BSI's) recommended symbols where appropriate.

1.11 Some Rules for the Use of Colour

1. Do not add colour unnecessarily, but only if its inclusion enhances the quality and meaning of your drawings.
2. Use care and discretion when including colour.

3. In general it is best to avoid heavy, bright colours and to use thin, clear colours.
4. Colouring with colour pencils is often quite sufficient, although water-colour washes and marker colours may be preferable for some graphics.
5. When answering examination questions, it is advisable not to colour your answers unless the question specifically asks for the use of colour in the answer. Extra marks are usually not awarded for colour work not asked for.
6. When sitting for an examination a set of colour pencils and a few colour pens should be taken into the examination room.

1.12 Some Rules for Answering Examination Questions

1. The instructions at the beginning of examination papers must be read and then followed. The **rubric**, as this part of the paper is called, tells you which of the questions to answer; how long you have; and where to place your answers on the papers, together with other similar instructions. Marks in examinations are frequently lost through failure to read the rubric.
2. Read each question and make sure you understand it fully **before** you commence answering it.
3. Do **not** add details to your answer not asked for in the question. Not only will such unasked-for details gain you no marks, but also you will be losing marks because of the time lost in drawing such unasked-for material.
4. **Always** attempt answering compulsory questions. When you become stuck, then go on to the next question. Do not worry about not being able to answer all questions fully. It is surprising how many marks can be gained, even with a number of answers, none of them fully complete.

1.13 British Standards Institution's Publications

Candidates should use symbols and other details from the following BSI publications:

BS 1192   *Recommendations for Building Drawing Practice*;
PD 7308   *Engineering Drawing Practice for Schools and Colleges*;
PD 7307   *Graphical Symbols for use in Schools and Colleges*;
BS 4058   *Data Processing Flow Chart Symbols, Rules and Conventions*.

1.14 Starter Drawings

All examination papers in this subject use **starters**. A question is set and printed with the question is a drawing which contains part of the required answer. The candidate is expected to complete the answer on the given starter drawing.

In this book frequent use is made of starters. These are printed in black and the completion of the answer is printed in red.

1.15 Specimen Answers

In this book there are a large number of specimen answers to questions set at the level of GCSE in the subject. All these specimen answers have been printed in red.

1.16 How to Make Best Use of this Book

Readers are advised to work through this book in the following manner:

1. Read the explanations of drawing constructions and techniques and work through the associated drawings;
2. Work the Worked Examples;
3. Read the notes on Have you Observed The Following Drawing Procedures given at the end of each chapter;
4. Work the Exercises given in each chapter;
5. Do not look at the solution to an exercise in Chapter 15, until you have attempted working a correct solution yourself.

2 Constructional Geometry

Success in Graphical Communication relies upon a knowledge of simple geometrical constructions. In this chapter all construction lines are red.

2.1 Straight Lines

(a) To Bisect a Line (Fig. 2.2)

Set a compass to about $\frac{2}{3}$ of AB
With A as centre draw arcs a
With B as centre draw arcs b
C is the centre of AB

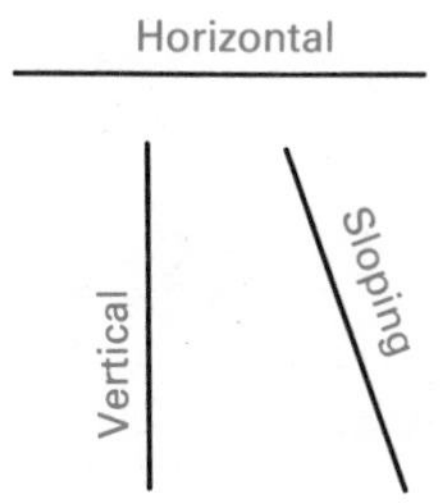

Horizontal

Vertical

Sloping

Figure 2.1 Straight lines

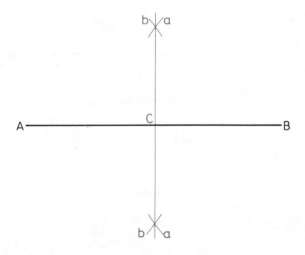

Figure 2.2 To bisect a line

(b) To Draw Parallel Lines (Fig. 2.4)

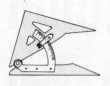

Place a set square on a straightedge on line CD
Move the set square along the straightedge to draw lines EF and GH
Note: An adjustable set square can be used (Fig. 2.3).

Figure 2.3
An adjustable set square

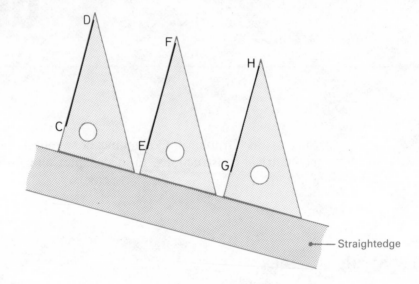

Figure 2.4   To draw parallel lines

(c) To Divide a Line into Equal Parts (Fig. 2.5)

Draw JL at any angle to JK
Mark 1 to 5 at equal spacing with a compass
Join 5 to K
Draw parallels through 1 to 4

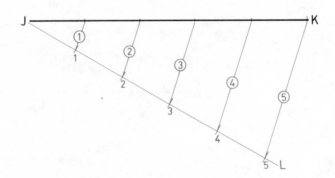

Figure 2.5   To divide a line into equal parts

(d) To Draw a Scale of 1:5 to Read up to 200 cm (Fig. 2.6)

Draw a line 20 cm (200 mm) long
Divide the line into 10 equal parts
Divide the first part of the line into 10 parts
Number as shown

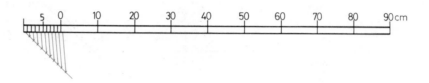

Figure 2.6 To draw a scale of 1:5 to read up to 200 cm

2.2 Angles

There are 360 degrees (360°) in a circle.
Angles can be right angled, acute, obtuse or reflex (Fig. 2.7).

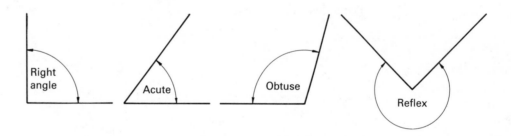

Figure 2.7 Angles

Angles of 30°, 60° and 90° can be easily drawn with a 30°, 60° set square (Fig. 2.8).

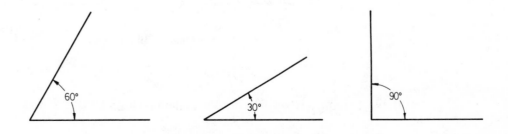

Figure 2.8 Set square angles

Angles of 45° can be easily drawn with a 45° set square.
Other angles may be drawn with a protractor (Fig. 2.9).

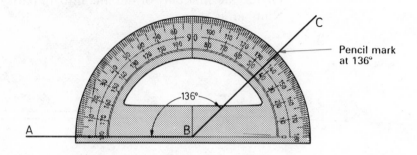

Figure 2.9 Angle drawn with a protractor

2.3 Triangles

The three angles of a triangle add up to 180°.
There are four types of triangle (Fig. 2.10):
    Equilateral — all sides equal. All angles equal (each 60°)
    Isosceles — opposite angles equal. Opposite sides equal
    Right angles — one angle is a right angle (90°)
    Scalene — all sides of different lengths. All angles of different sizes
Triangles may be **acute** or **obtuse**.

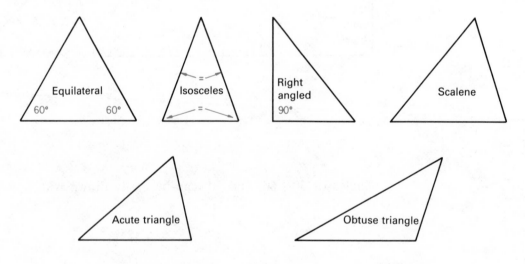

Figure 2.10 Triangles

(a) Circumscribed Circle to a Triangle (Fig. 2.11)

Bisect any two sides.
C, where the bisectors cross is the centre of the circumscribing circle.

(b) Inscribed Circle to a Triangle (Fig. 2.11)

Bisect any two angles.

I, where the bisectors meet is the centre of the inscribing circles.

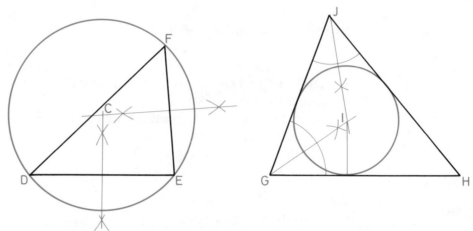

Figure 2.11 Circumscribing and inscribing circles to triangles

(c) The Angle Within a Semi-circle is a Right Angle (Fig.2.12)

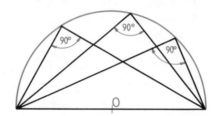

Figure 2.12 The angle in a semi-circle is a right angle

2.4 Quadrilaterals (Fig. 2.13)

Quadrilaterals have four sides.

The four angles of a quadrilateral add up to 360°.

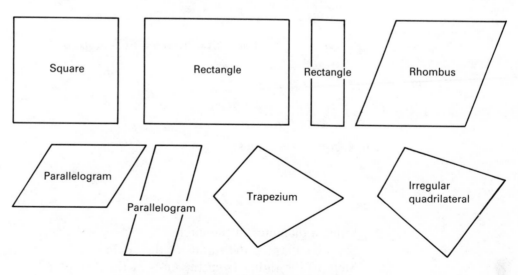

Figure 2.13 Types of quadrilateral

2.5 To Construct a Regular Pentagon

A pentagon has five sides

(a) Given Side Length (Fig. 2.14)

Draw a base EA
Draw 45° and 60° angles at both E and A
Bisect PR to give O
Set a compass to OA and draw a circle centred at O
Step off EA around the circle
Complete the pentagon

(b) Given the Circumscribing Circle (Fig. 2.14)

Draw the circle diameter JN
Construct to find L — $\frac{2}{5}$ of JN
With a compass set to JN draw arcs from J and from N to meet at M
Draw ML and produce to K on the circle
JK is one side of the required pentagon

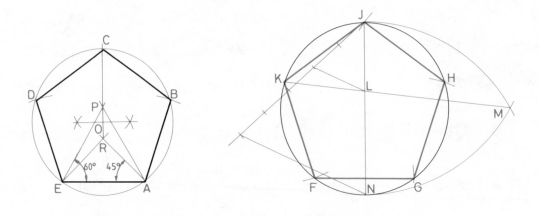

Figure 2.14   To construct a regular pentagon

2.6 To Construct a Regular Hexagon

A hexagon has six sides.

(a) Within a Circle (Fig. 2.15)

Draw a diameter of the circle
Set a compass to the radius of the circle
Step off the radius from the ends of the diameter
Complete the hexagon

(b) **With a Set Square (Fig. 2.15)**

Draw a circle of hexagon side radius
Draw a diameter of the circle
Complete the hexagon with a set square

(c) **Circumscribing a Circle (Fig. 2.15)**

Draw the hexagon with the aid of a set square as shown.

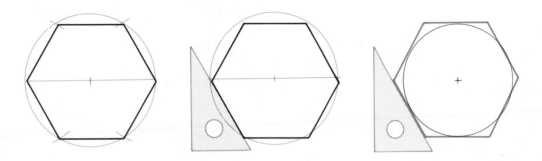

Figure 2.15   To construct a regular hexagon

2.7   To Construct Regular Heptagons

A heptagon has seven sides.

(a) **Given Side Length (Fig. 2.16)**

Use the first stages of the method as for regular pentagons (Section 2.5(a))
Measure the length BC from C to give D
D is the centre of the circle circumscribing the regular heptagon

(b) **Given the Circumscribing Circle (Fig. 2.16)**

Use the same method as for the pentagon (Section 2.5(b)), except to take $\frac{2}{7}$ of the diameter of the circle instead of $\frac{2}{5}$.

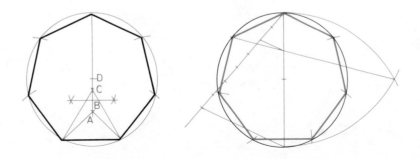

Figure 2.16   To construct regular heptagons

13

2.8 To Construct Regular Octagons

An octagon has eight sides.

(a) Given Side Length (Fig. 2.17)

Use a 45° set square and measure off the side lengths with the aid of a compass.

(b) Within a Square (Fig. 2.17)

Draw the diagonals of the square
Set a compass to the length of the distance of any corner of the square to the centre where the diagonals cross
Draw arcs as shown
Complete the regular octagon

(c) Circumscribing a Circle (Fig. 2.17)

Use a 45° set square as shown.

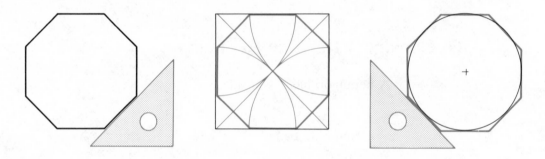

Figure 2.17 To construct regular octagons

2.9 Circles

The names of parts of a circle are given in Fig. 2.18.

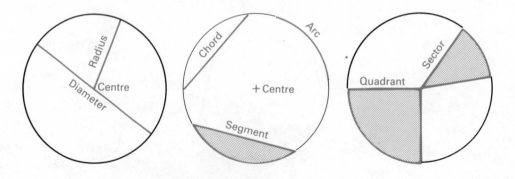

Figure 2.18 Part of a circle

(a) To Find the Centre of a Circle (Fig. 2.19)

Select any three points A, B and C
Bisect AB and BC to find O, the required centre

(b) To Find the Centre of an Arc (Fig. 2.19)

See Section 2.9(a) above.

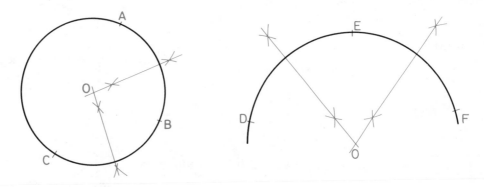

Figure 2.19   To find the centre of a circle or of an arc

(c) To Draw Touching Arcs of Circles (Fig. 2.20)

Either **add** the radii for arcs touching **externally**, or **subtract** the radii for arcs touching **internally**.

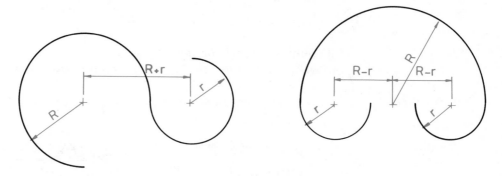

Figure 2.20   To draw touching arcs of circles

(d) Straight Line Tangents at Points on a Circle (Fig. 2.21)

Join T to the centre C
Draw the 90° angle at T to give the required tangent

(e) Straight Line Tangents to a Circle from a Point Outside (Fig. 2.21)

Join PO and bisect
Draw the semi-circle on PO, crossing the original circle at T
Join PT — the required tangent

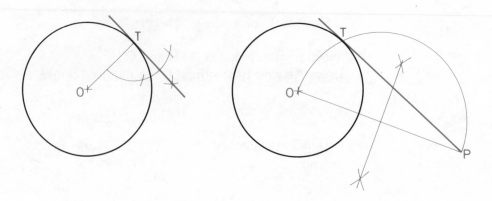

Figure 2.21 Straight line tangents to a circle

2.10 Ellipses

(a) To Construct an Ellipse (Fig. 2.22)

Draw the **major** and **minor** axes
Draw the major and minor auxiliary circles
Draw a number of diameters crossing both circles
Where each diameter meets the circles, draw lines parallel to the major and minor axes
Where these lines meet are points on the ellipse

(b) To Find the Foci of an Ellipse (Fig. 2.22)

Set a compass to half the major axis
From where the minor axis meets the ellipse draw arcs crossing the major axis

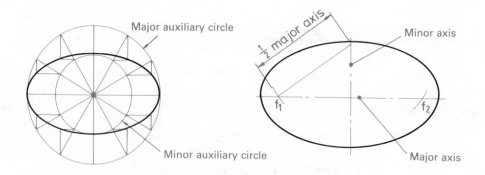

Figure 2.22 To construct an ellipse

(c) To Construct a Tangent Touching an Ellipse (Fig. 2.23)

Find the foci f_1 and f_2
Draw lines from the foci through T
Bisect the angle between the two lines to give the tangent
Note: The **Normal** is at right angles to the tangent.

(d) To Draw a Line Parallel to an Ellipse (Fig. 2.23)

Set a compass to the distance by which the line is to be parallel to the ellipse
From a number of points on the ellipse draw arcs
Draw curve touching these arcs

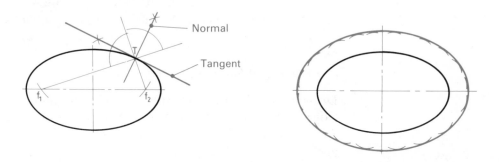

Figure 2.23 To find the foci of an ellipse and to draw a parallel to an ellipse

(e) To Draw an Ellipse with a Trammel (Fig. 2.24)

Measure half of each axis along the edge of a piece of paper as shown
    With A moved on the minor axis and B moved on the major axis, make a
number of pencil marks at C
Draw a curve through the points C

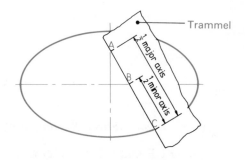

Figure 2.24 To draw an ellipse with a trammel

2.11 Areas

(a) Areas of Plane Figures (Fig. 2.25)

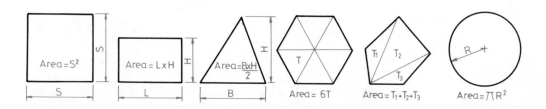

Figure 2.25 Areas of plane figures

(b) Areas of Irregular Figures (Fig. 2.26)

(i) *Mid-ordinate Method*

Mark off centimetre divisions along the length of the figure
Draw ordinates through the centres of each centimetre division
Measure the length of each ordinate on the figure
Add the lengths together to find the area in square centimetres (sq cm or cm^2)

(ii) *Counting of Squares Method*

Draw a grid of centimetre squares over the figure
Count the number of whole squares of the grid within the figure
Add together all the parts of squares within the figure to obtain an approximate number of squares
Add together the two numbers so obtained

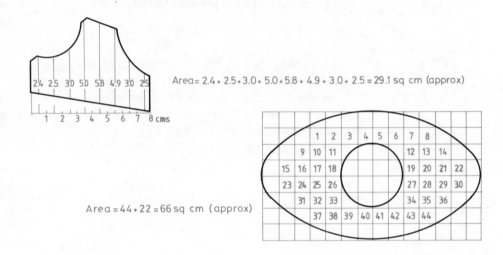

Area = 2.4 + 2.5 + 3.0 + 5.0 + 5.8 + 4.9 + 3.0 + 2.5 = 29.1 sq cm (approx)

Area = 44 + 22 = 66 sq cm (approx)

Figure 2.26   Areas of irregular figures

(iii) *By Reducing to a Rectangle of Equal Area (Fig. 2.27)*

Draw EF and CG parallel to AD and BD
The triangle DFG is of equal area to the original figure
Bisect the height of triangle DFG
Complete the rectangle FGHJ which is of equal area to the original figure
Measure the rectangle sides and multiply together to obtain the required area

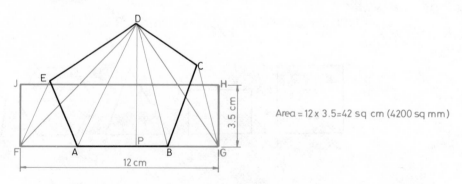

Area = 12 x 3.5 = 42 sq cm (4200 sq mm)

Figure 2.27   Reducing a plane figure to a rectangle of the same area

18

2.12 Reducing and Enlarging Figures in Ratio to Their Side Lengths (Fig.2.28)

Divide the base of the figure into the required ratio (Section 2.1(c))
Draw the diagonals AC, AD and AE
Draw B₁, CD, DE and EF parallel to the sides of the original figure
Produce F₁ to F
Note: The enlarging of a figure in ratio to its sides is carried out in a similar manner.

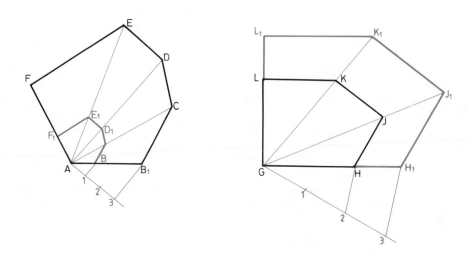

Figure 2.28 Reducing and enlarging figures in a ratio of their side lengths

2.13 To Construct a Parabolic Curve (Fig. 2.29)

(a) As a Locus Curve

A parabola is the locus of a point as it moves so as to be always the same distance from a fixed **focus** f as it is from a fixed line dd the **directrix**.

Draw the directrix dd
Mark f at the required distance along the axis AB
Draw a number of lines parallel to dd
Set a compass to the lengths, in turn, that each is distant from dd
With the compass centred at f draw arcs across each of the lines parallel to dd, in turn
Draw a fair curve through the points so obtained

(b) Within a Rectangle

Bisect CD and draw a vertical centre line
Divide the two parts of CD each into 5 parts (say)
Divide the sides CF and DE into the same number of parts — in this example, 5 parts
Draw lines as shown
Draw a fair curve through the intersecting lines to obtain the parabola

19

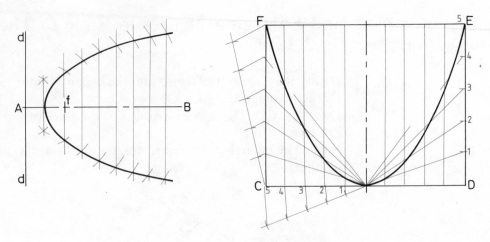

Figure 2.29 To construct a parabolic curve

2.14 Worked Examples

Worked Example 2.1 (Fig. 2.30)

Bisect the line AB. Using the same construction method divide the line CD into 4 equal parts.

Solution 2.1

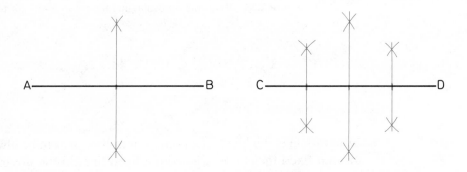

Figure 2.30 Worked Example 2.1

Worked Example 2.2 (Fig. 2.31)

(a) Divide the line AB into 9 equal parts;
(b) Divide the line CD into the ratio 2:3.

Solution 2.2

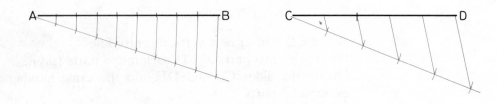

Figure 2.31 Worked Example 2.2

Worked Example 2.3 (Fig. 2.32)

Using the line AB as a base, construct a scale of 1:2.5 to read in centimetres up to 50 cm.

Solution 2.3

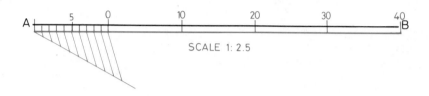

Figure 2.32   Worked Example 2.3

Worked Example 2.4 (Fig. 2.33)

State the length AC.

Solution 2.4

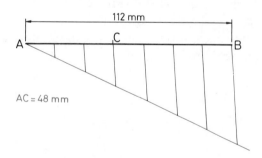

Figure 2.33   Worked Example 2.4

Worked Example 2.5 (Fig. 2.34)

On the given lines construct the following angles:
    ABC = 60°; EDF = 45°; GHJ = 15°;
    LKM = 105°

Solution 2.5

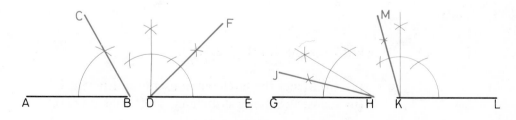

Figure 2.34   Worked Example 2.5

Worked Example 2.6 (Fig. 2.35)

  (a) On the line AB draw the triangle in which:
      AC = 80 mm; and BC = 55 mm.
  (b) On the line DE construct the triangle DEF in which the angle at D is 60°
      and EF = 65 mm. Show your construction for the angle at D.

Solution 2.6

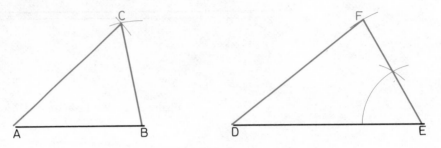

Figure 2.35   Worked Example 2.6

Worked Example 2.7 (Fig. 2.36)

Name each of the triangles A to G. State also which of the 7 triangles are acute,
obtuse or right angled.

Solution 2.7

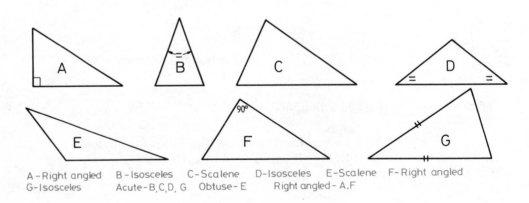

A – Right angled   B – Isosceles   C – Scalene   D – Isosceles   E – Scalene   F – Right angled
G – Isosceles   Acute – B, C, D, G   Obtuse – E   Right angled – A, F

Figure 2.36   Worked Example 2.7

Worked Example 2.8 (Fig. 2.37)

  (a) Construct the circle circumscribing triangle DEF.
  (b) Construct the inscribing circle of triangle GHJ.

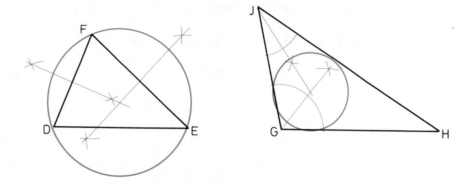

Figure 2.37 Worked Example 2.8

Worked Example 2.9

(a) Construct the star shape given in Fig. 2.38.
(b) Construct the interweaving band given in Fig. 2.39.

Solution 2.9 (Fig. 2.40)

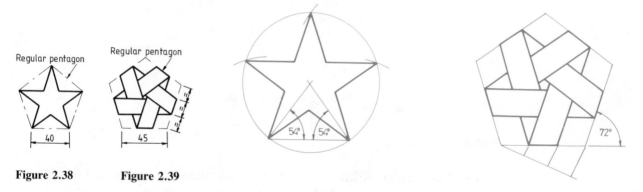

Figure 2.38   **Figure 2.39**

Figure 2.40   Worked Example 2.9

Worked Example 2.10 (Fig. 2.41)

(a) Construct a regular hexagon with sides of the same length as the radius of the circle C.
(b) Construct a regular hexagon circumscribing the circle O.

Solution 2.10

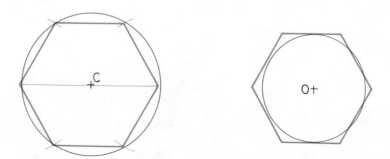

Figure 2.41   Worked Example 2.10

Worked Example 2.11

(a) Construct the outline given in Fig. 2.42. All constructions must be shown.

(b) Draw the circle which passes through the points A, B and C.

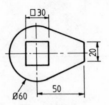

Figure 2.42

Solution 2.11 (Fig. 2.43)

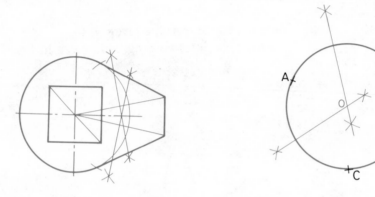

Figure 2.43 Worked Example 2.11

Worked Example 2.12

(a) Using geometrical constructions, draw the shape given in Fig. 2.44.

(b) Construct an arc which starts at A, passes through C and finishes at B.

Solution 2.12 (Fig. 2.45)

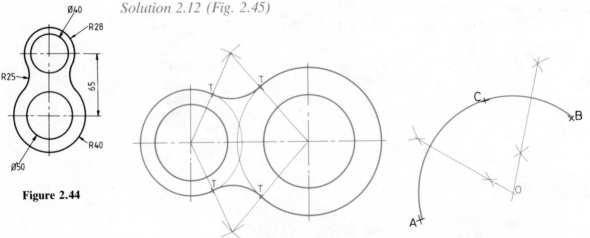

Figure 2.44

Figure 2.45 Worked Example 2.12

24

2.15 Exercises

2.1
Construct the triangle ABC, in which:
AB = 90 mm; AC = 50 mm and the angle C is 90°.
2.2
In Fig. 2.46:

- (a) Which line is a chord?
- (b) Which line is a radius?
- (c) Which line is a diameter?
- (d) Which line is a tangent?
- (e) Name part E
- (f) Name part F
- (g) Name part G
- (h) Name part H

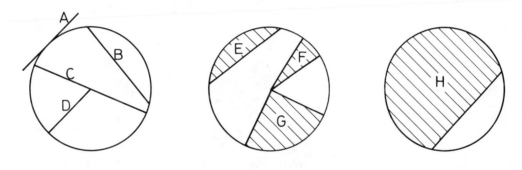

Figure 2.46   Exercise 2.2

2.3
In Fig. 2.47:

- (a) Name the 2 lines AB and CD
- (b) Find, by construction, the foci of the ellipse
- (c) Construct a circle of 40 mm diameter which touches the ellipse at T.

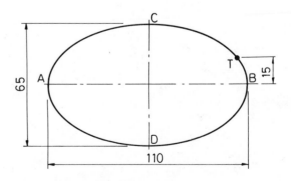

Figure 2.47   Exercise 2.3

2.4
State the areas of the figures A, B, C, D, E and F in Fig. 2.48. Show how you arrived at your answers.

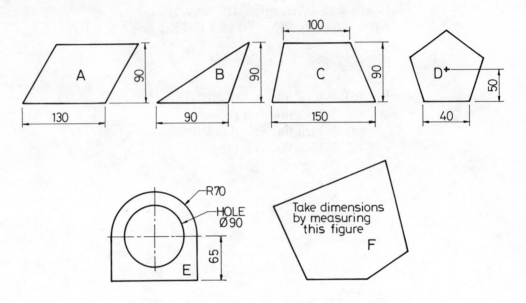

Figure 2.48 Exercise 2.4

2.5
Draw the given figure 2.49, scale 1:1. Calculate its area using a graphical method.

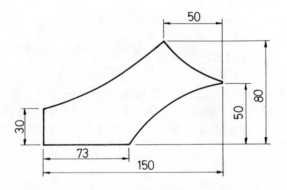

Figure 2.49 Exercise 2.5

2.6

Draw Fig. 2.50, scale 1:100. Using a graphical method, calculate the area of the lawn to the nearest 0.1 square metre.

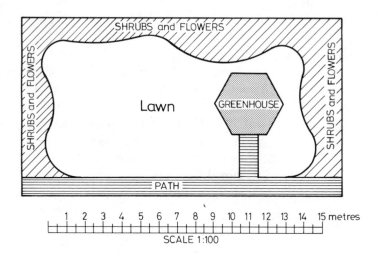

Figure 2.50 Exercise 2.6

2.7

Reduce the given letter E, Fig. 2.51, proportionally by scale 2:3.

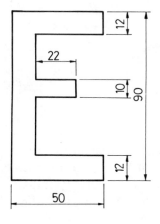

Figure 2.51 Exercise 2.7

2.8

Fig. 2.52 shows a trade plate for a firm with the name **STED**. The plate is to be enlarged by scale 3:2. Construct the enlarged outline of the plate.

Figure 2.52 Exercise 2.8

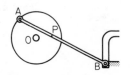

Figure 2.53 Exercise 2.9

27

2.9

Fig. 2.53 shows part of a mechanism for driving a power hacksaw. As the wheel OA rotates, a crank AB pivoted at A, drives the end of the link B in a horizontal line.

On the given drawing, construct the locus of the point P on the crank AB.

2.10

Fig. 2.54. A crank OA is pivoted at a fixed position O in such a manner as to allow the end A to rotate freely in a circle. The end A is attached to a link AB. AB can slide within a slider at F. The end B of the link AB is attached to a second link BC. BC can slide within a slider at G. Both the sliders F and G are in fixed positions, but can rotate freely.

Plot the loci of the ends B and C of the two links AB and BC. **OA** = 40 mm; **AB** = 140 mm; **BC** = 110 mm.

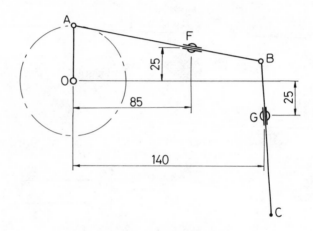

Figure 2.54   Exercise 2.10

2.11

Fig. 2.55 is a small-scale sectional drawing through a spotlight, showing the outline of both the reflector and the lens of the light.

Make an accurate, full-size drawing of the sectional outline showing all constructions used for finding the curves of the parabola and the arc.

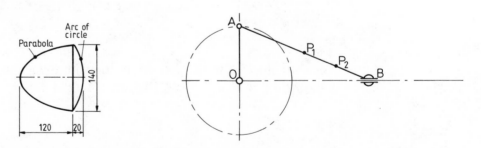

Figure 2.55   Exercise 2.11   **Figure 2.56**   Exercise 2.12

2.12

A crank OA rotates about a fixed pivot at O. A link AB, pivoted at A, is constrained to move along the horizontal line through A by a slider at B. Fig. 2.56.

Plot the loci of the 2 points P_1 and P_2 on the link AB as A rotates through a complete circle.

AO = 40 mm; AB = 100 mm;
AP_1 = 50 mm; AP_2 = 75 mm

2.13

Two air ducting pipes, A and B, rest on brackets as shown in Fig. 2.57. Pipe A is 70 mm diameter. Pipe B also touches the top bracket.

(a) By construction find the centre of pipe A and draw the pipe.
(b) By construction find the centre of pipe B and draw the pipe.

(SEG Specimen Question)

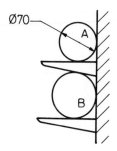

Figure 2.57   Exercise 2.13

2.16   Worked Examples

Worked Example 2.13

The crank OB in Fig. 2.58 rotates about point O and is pin jointed to the rod PC at B. C is constrained to move along a quarter ellipse as shown. The cam is positioned to lie in the path of the end of the rod P and is free to rock about its shaft S.

Draw, full size, in the positions indicated:

(a) The quarter ellipse;

(b) The locus of point P for one complete revolution of the crank OB;

(c) The outline of the cam showing all tangent points marked thus O.

All construction lines for obtaining the quarter ellipse, the locus, arc centres and tangent points must be shown.

(Scottish)

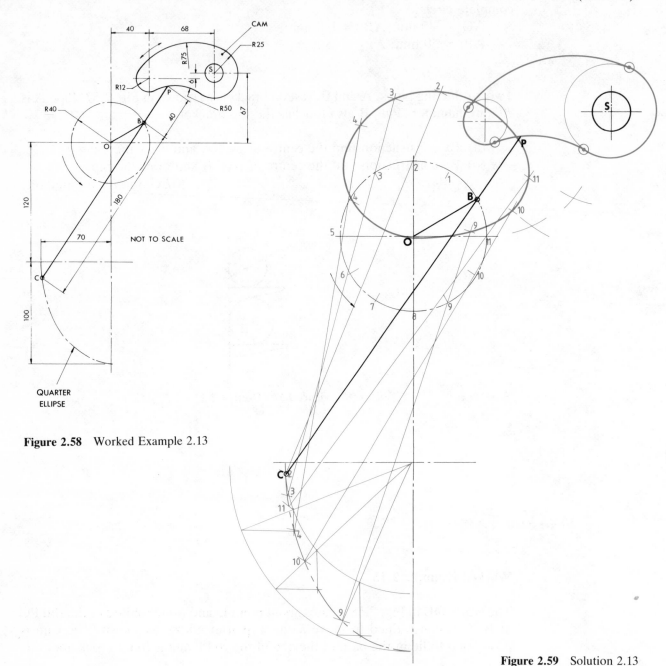

Figure 2.58 Worked Example 2.13

Figure 2.59 Solution 2.13

Solution 2.13

Draw the quarter ellipse — auxiliary circle method (Section 2.10).

Complete the cam. The 75 mm radius centre is found by R−r; the 50 mm radius is found by R+r (Section 2.9).

Divide circle OB into 12 parts — 30°60° set square.

With a compass set at 180 mm strike arcs from these circle points on to the quarter ellipse.

Draw lines from these points on the quarter ellipse through the points on the circle.

Set a compass to 40 mm and from the points on the circle OB strike arcs to give points on the locus of P.

Draw the locus curve.

Note: for the sake of clarity, only 6 of the 11 locus plot lines have been included in the given solution.

Worked Example 2.14

A standard construction for an open ended spanner with a bolt shown in position is given in Fig. 2.60.

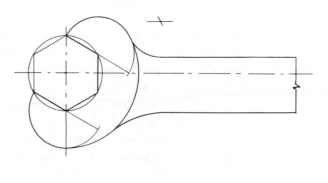

Figure 2.60 Worked Example 2.14

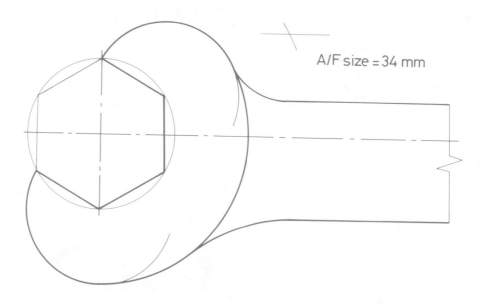

A/F size = 34 mm

Figure 2.61 Solution 2.14

(a) State the A/F measurement of the spanner.

(b) Using the standard construction shown, draw a similar spanner having an A/F dimension of 68 mm.

(LREB)

Solution 2.14

Note that the required A/F size is 34 mm, thus the solution is drawn with measurements at twice those of the given drawing.

Have You Observed the Following Drawing Procedures?

1. In examinations **always** start answering geometrical questions, even if you are not sure of all the constructions needed. Remember that some marks can be gained for answers which are only partly completed. Even by just starting an answer, marks may be gained.

2. Use thin construction lines for constructions, but line-in all of a completed answer using thick outline lines.

3. **All** construction lines **must** be shown when answering questions involving geometrical constructions. Do **not** erase them. Examiners will be awarding marks for each part of all geometrical constructions. If you erase your constructions, the examiner will not be able to give you any of the marks available for them.

4. You cannot expect to gain marks by guessing at constructions, but marks will still be awarded for a correct answer, even if part of the construction has not been drawn correctly.

3 Orthographic Projection

3.1 Views and Plans

A storage box is shown in the photograph Fig. 3.1.

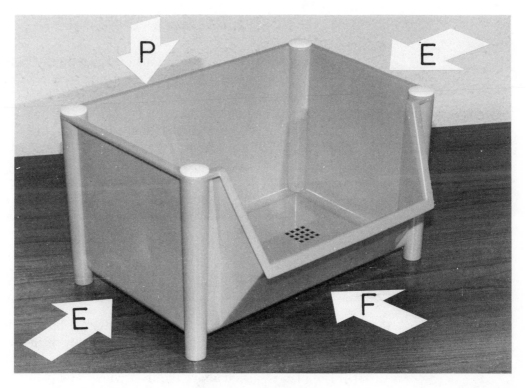

Figure 3.1 A storage box

(a) Front Views

A **front view** is a drawing of what is seen when an article is looked at in the direction of the arrow F.

(b) End Views

End views are drawings of what can be seen when an article is looked at in the direction of the arrows E.

(c) Plans

A **plan** is a drawing of what is seen when an article is looked at in the direction of the arrow P.

3.2 Rules

(a) Views may be called **elevations**.
(b) When drawing views and plans, the problems of perspective are ignored. (See Section 8.11.)
(c) Views and plans are drawn in line with each other.
(d) Orthographic projections can be drawn in either of two **Angles** — First Angle projection or Third Angle projection.

3.3 First Angle Projection

Fig. 3.2 is a First Angle projection of the storage box shown in the Fig. 3.1. Note the following:

(a) The end view (or end elevation) is drawn on the **right-hand side** of the front view. It is the view seen when the box is viewed as if looked at from the **left**.
(b) If the box had been looked at as if from the right, then the end view would have been drawn on the left-hand side of the front view.
(c) The end view (or elevation) is **in line** with the front view.
(d) The plan is drawn **underneath** the front view.
(e) Both end view and plan face **outwards** from the front view.
(f) Note the British Standard Institution's First Angle symbol of projection. The symbol is itself a First Angle projection of the frustum of a cone (see Section 4.1).

3.4 Third Angle Projection

Fig. 3.3 is a Third Angle projection of the storage box. Note the following:

(a) The end view is drawn on the **left-hand side** of the front view. It is the view seen when the box is viewed as if looked at from the **left**.
(b) The plan is placed **above** the front view. The plan is what is seen when the box is viewed as if looked at from **above**.
(c) Both end view and plan face **inwards** towards the front view.
(d) Note the British Standard Institution's Third Angle symbol of projection.

3.5 Types of Lines

In the drawings Fig. 3.2 and Fig. 3.3, the following types of lines can be seen:

(a) *Outline lines* — the outlines of all views and plans are drawn with **thick** lines.
(b) *Centre lines* — drawn through the centre of all circular parts — are **thin, broken** lines.
(c) *Hidden detail lines* — which show details which cannot be seen from the outside of the article being drawn — are **thin, dashed** lines.

The thickness of lines varies according to the size of the paper being used. In general, when making drawings on sheets of A2 size, **thick lines** should be about

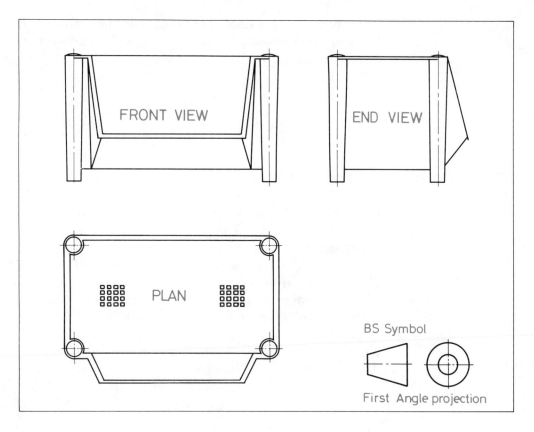

Figure 3.2 A First Angle orthographic projection

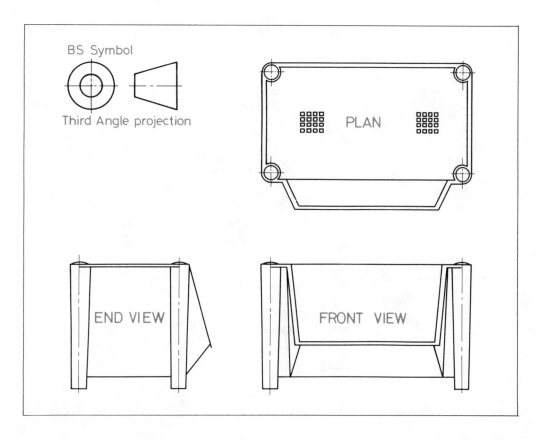

Figure 3.3 A Third Angle orthographic projection

0.7 mm thick and **thin lines** about 0.35 mm thick. On smaller or larger sheets, lines should be thinner or thicker than 0.7 mm and 0.35 mm.

More information is given in the chapter dealing with Engineering Drawing (Chapter 10).

3.6 Layouts of Orthographic Projections

Fig. 3.4 shows a simple method of achieving good sheet layout when drawing an orthographic projection. The procedure is to first work out the positions of the various views and plan in the projection, so that the 3 lengths **A** are approximately equal and also the lengths **B** are approximately equal. This can be worked out using simple arithmetic. Add together the widths of the front and end views, subtract the number arrived at from the width of the sheet between its margins, then divide the difference by 3. Repeat with the front view and plan to find the length of **B**.

When the positions for the views and plan on the sheet have been worked out in this way, details from the front view can be projected into the end view via a line drawn with a 45° set square. The lines 1, 2, 3 and 4 indicate how details from the front view have been projected into the plan and then from the plan into the end view.

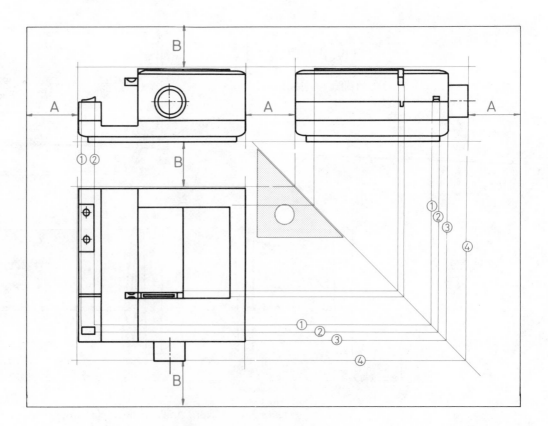

Figure 3.4 First Angle projection of a transparency projector

3.7 Dimensions

Fig. 3.5 shows how dimensions are included in an orthographic projection.

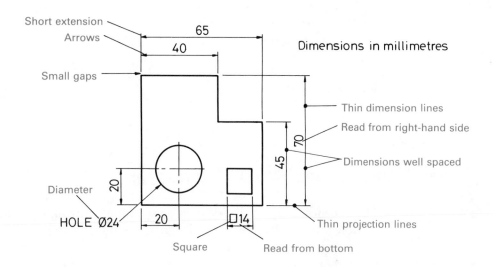

Figure 3.5 Dimensions

3.8 Simple Sectional Views

The use of sectional views allows drawings to be made which describe the shape of parts which cannot be seen from the outside of an article. In a sectional view, it is imagined that a cut has been made through an article and the cut surfaces then drawn as views. Fig. 3.6 is an example of a simple sectional view. Such views are normally referred to as Section AA, Section BB, etc. On drawings sections are normally labelled **A-A**, **B-B** etc. Note the following in Fig. 3.6 and Fig. 3.7.

    (a) The edge of the section cutting plane is drawn as a centre line, ending with thick lines.

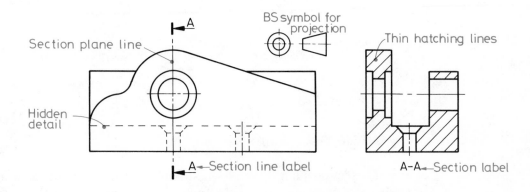

Figure 3.6 A simple sectional view

(b) The direction in which the section is viewed is indicated by arrows. These arrows are labelled with letters.

(c) The surfaces cut by the section plane are hatched with lines drawn at 45° and about 4 mm apart. Both the angle and the spacing may be varied if necessary.

(d) Adjacent parts cut by the section plant are hatched with lines at alternate angles.

(e) The sectional view is labelled — **A-A**, **B-B** for example. These letters correspond to the letters at the ends of the section cutting plane line.

3.9   Types of Sectional View

The following are various types of sectional drawings. Some of these types of section are usually only seen in engineering drawings. See Chapter 10.

(a) Section Taken Along a Centre Line

When the section plane cuts through an article centrally there is no need to include the section cutting plane line. This is because it is quite obvious where the cutting plane is intended to be. Example: Fig. 3.7.

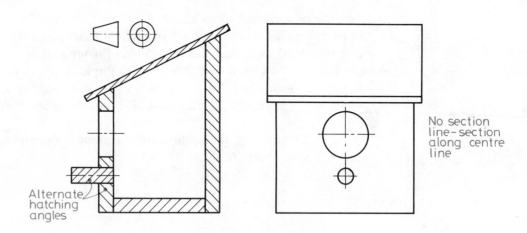

Figure 3.7   A sectional view taken on a centre line

(b) Outside Views Within Sections

When a section plane passes longitudinally through parts such as nuts, bolts, washers, rivets, keys, webs, ribs and other features such as these, these parts are drawn as outside views within the sectional view. Example: Fig. 3.8.

38

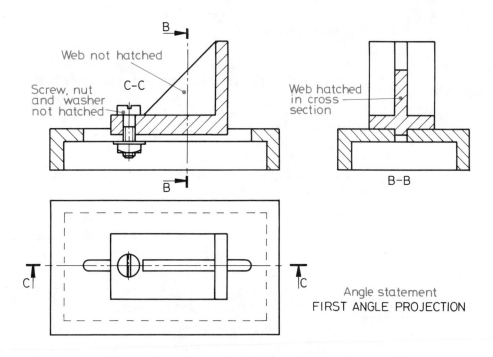

Figure 3.8 Outside views within a section

(c) Half Sections

If a section is to be drawn of a part which is symmetrical about a centre line, a half section may give as much information about the internal shape of the part as is required. Example: Fig. 3.9.

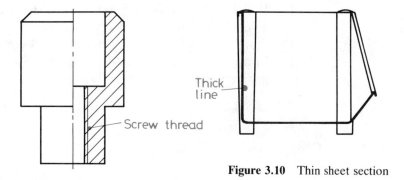

Figure 3.10 Thin sheet section

Figure 3.9 A half section

3.10 Other Types of Section

(a) Thin Sheet Material Sections

Example: Fig. 3.10 (a sectional cut through the storage box shown in Fig. 3.1).
Note: The cut surfaces are drawn with thicker lines than outline lines.

(b) Removed Sections

Example: part of Fig. 3.11.

    Note: half of the view is sectioned, the other half being an outside view.

(c) Part Sections

Example: part of Fig. 3.11.

    Note: Part of the view has been drawn as if a piece has been broken out to reveal the inner shape.

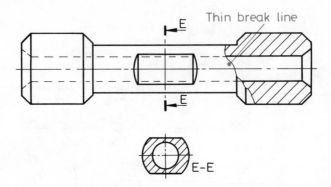

Figure 3.11   Removed and part sections ·

3.11 Worked Examples

Worked Example 3.1 (Fig. 3.12)

    (a) Which of the pictorial views A, B, C, D or E is the correct shape for the given 3-view orthographic projection?

    (b) State the angle of projection of the 3-view orthographic projection.

    (c) In a suitable position add the British Standard Institution's symbol of projection to the given drawing.

Solution 3.1

Given in red (Fig. 3.12)

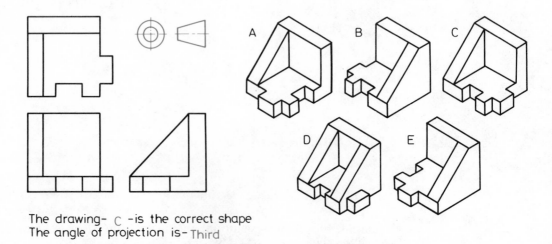

The drawing- C -is the correct shape
The angle of projection is- Third

Figure 3.12   Worked Example 3.1

Worked Example 3.2 (Fig. 3.14)

A block with a tapered hole is shown in Fig. 3.13. A front and an end elevation of the block are given in Third Angle projection. Add to these two elevations a plan as seen in the direction of the arrow P.

Solution 3.2

Given in red (Fig. 3.14).

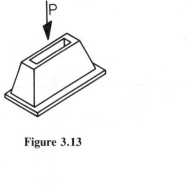

Figure 3.13

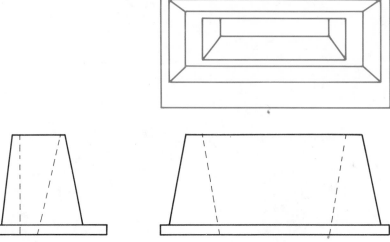

Figure 3.14   Worked Example 3.2

Worked Example 3.3 (Fig. 3.15)

(a) A front view and a plan of a wing nut are given drawn on a 5 mm square grid. Add, in First Angle projection, an end view as seen in the direction of the arrow. Add the BS symbol of projection to the drawing.

(b) Fig. 3.16 is a drawing of a machine part. A front elevation and the outline of the plan of the part have been drawn on a 5 mm square grid in Third Angle projection. On the grid, complete the plan and add an end elevation as seen in the direction of the arrow E. Add the BS symbol for Third Angle projection to the drawing.

Given in red (Fig. 3.15).

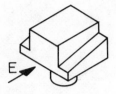

Figure 3.16

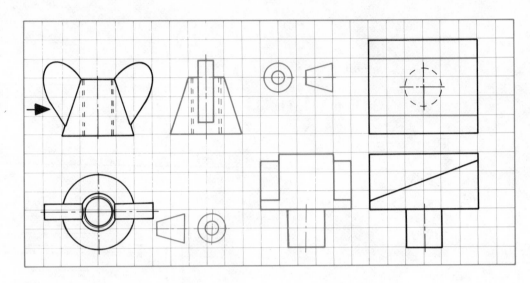

Figure 3.15   Worked Example 3.3

Worked Example 3.4 (Fig. 3.17)

A front view and a plan of a part from a machine are given. Add the sectional view on A-A.

Solution 3.4

Given in red (Fig. 3.17).

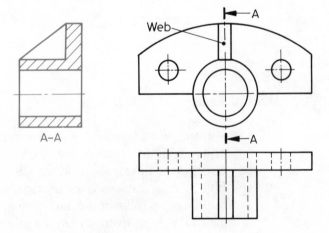

Figure 3.17   Worked Example 3.4

Worked Example 3.5 (Fig. 3.18)

The given drawing is a 2-view Third Angle projection of a numbered wheel support. Add to the drawing a correctly projected Section S-S.

Solution 3.5

Given in red (Fig. 3.18)

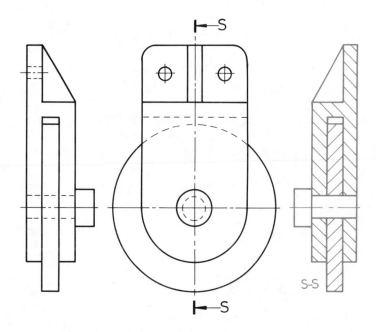

Figure 3.18   Worked Example 3.5

Worked Example 3.6 (Fig. 3.19)

A front elevation and an end elevation of a brake lever and its pivot pin are given in First Angle projection. Add to the drawing, in correct projection, the Sectional plan C-C.

Solution 3.6

Given in red (Fig. 3.19).

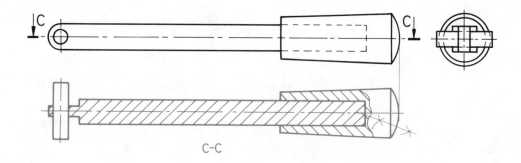

Figure 3.19   Worked Example 3.6

43

Worked Example 3.7 (Fig. 3.20)

The six drawings of Fig. 3.20 are incomplete First or Third Angle projections of various solids. Lines are missing from each of the projections. Complete the drawings by adding all missing lines. State in each box whether the projections are in First or Third Angle.

Solution 3.7

Given in red (Fig. 3.20).

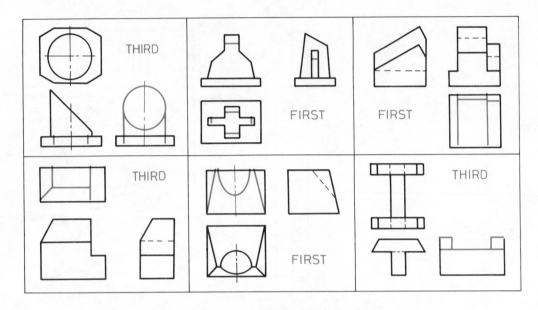

Figure 3.20   Worked Example 3.7

Worked Example 3.8 (Fig. 3.21)

Using instruments, draw full size and in first angle projection, three orthographic views of the blank propeller shaft shown in Fig. 3.21. Select your viewing position to show the shape to the best advantage and show hidden detail, if any, in each view.

(LEAG Specimen Question)

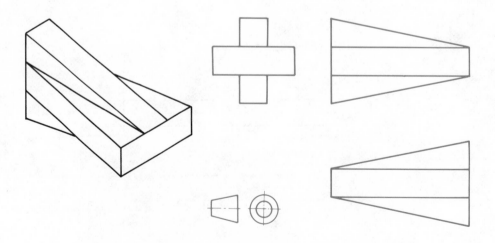

Figure 3.21

Given in red (Fig. 3.21).

3.12 Exercises

3.1

Fig. 3.22 is a drawing of the handle from an electric slide switch. Which of A, B, C, D or E of Fig. 3.23 is a correct plan for the switch?

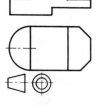

Figure 3.22

 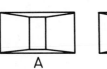

Figure 3.23 Exercise 3.1

3.2

Which of A, B, C or D of Fig. 3.24 is a correct pictorial drawing of the solid shown by the projection in Fig. 3.25?

Figure 3.25

Figure 3.24 Exercise 3.2

3.3

Which of the drawings A, B, C or D of Fig. 3.26 is a correct interpretation of the orthographic views given in Fig. 3.27?

Figure 3.27

 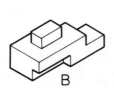 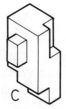

Figure 3.26 Exercise 3.3

3.4

Which of the drawings A, B, C, D, E, F, G or H of Fig. 3.28 is the correct end view to be placed in the position marked EE in Fig. 3.29?

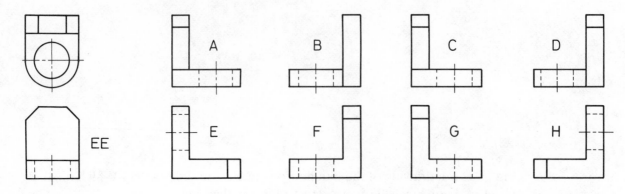

Figure 3.29

Figure 3.28   Exercise 3.4

3.5

Which of the four orthographic projections A, B, C or D of Fig. 3.30 is in Third Angle?

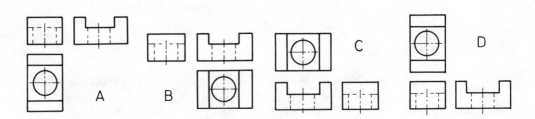

Figure 3.30   Exercise 3.4

3.6

Which of A, B, C or D of Fig. 3.31 is the correct sectional view S-S of Fig. 3.32?

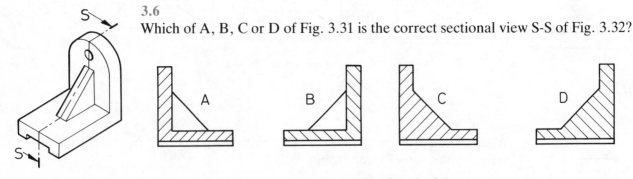

Figure 3.32

Figure 3.31   Exercise 3.6

3.7

The given three views in First Angle projection of Fig. 3.34 are correctly projected views of the solid shown in Fig. 3.33.
Answer the following:

   (a) Which lines in the front view represent the surfaces G and H in the plan?

(b) Which lines in the end view represent the surfaces A, B and C in the plan?

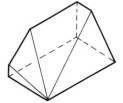

Figure 3.33

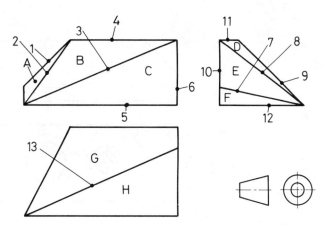

Figure 3.34 Exercise 3.7

3.8

Fig. 3.35 shows two views of a Clip. Add to the given drawing the sectional view on X-X.

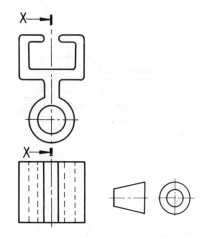

Figure 3.35 Exercise 3.8

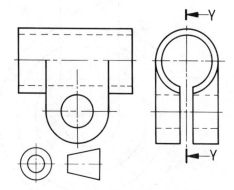

Figure 3.36 Exercise 3.9

3.9

Fig. 3.36 shows two views of a pipe clamping clip. Add to the given drawing the sectional view Y-Y.

47

3.10

Fig. 3.37 shows two views of a stand. Add to the two views the sectional view on A-A.

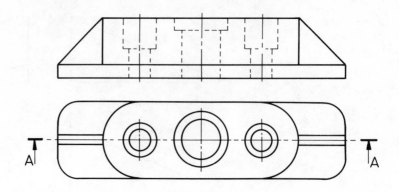

Figure 3.37 Exercise 3.10

3.11

Orthographic views of a stepped pulley are given in Fig. 3.38. Project the sectional view SS.

(Welsh)

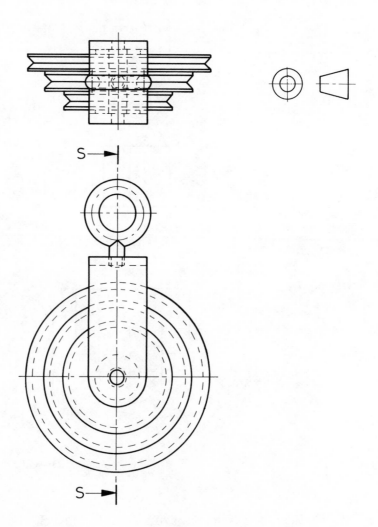

Figure 3.38 Exercise 3.11

Have You Observed the Following Drawing Procedures?

1. Make yourself familiar with both First and Third Angle orthographic projection.
2. Views may be called elevations.
3. Remember the basic rules for these projections:
   In **First** Angle:
   Plan is **below** front view;
   Plan and end view face **outwards** from the front view;
   End views are the views as seen when the front view is looked at from the other side to that in which the end view is placed.
   In **Third** Angle:
   Plan is **above** front view;
   Plan and end view face **inwards** towards front view;
   End views are the views as seen when the front view is looked at from the same side as that on which the end view is placed.
4. Views and plans must be **in line** with each other.
5. Do **not** mix First and Third Angle views or plans. In certain circumstances an arrow can be included with a view which has not been drawn in the same angle as other views, together with a note stating the direction of viewing. This does not generally apply in GCSE work in the subject.
6. Usually there is no need to show **how** you constructed views in orthographic projection questions, unless asked to do so. Erase construction lines.
7. All outline lines of orthographic projection drawings should be thick and black.
8. Draw all centre lines through circular parts.
9. Draw the British Standards Institution's symbols of projection to identify the angle you are using.
10. It is advisable to hatch those parts of sectional views showing parts which have been cut through, except for the exceptions — screws, bolts, nuts, ribs, webs, etc.

4 Geometrical Solids

4.1 Terms

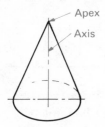

Figure 4.1 A right geometrical solid

Axis — the axis of a right geometrical solid lies along a line taken centrally and at right angles to the base of the solid (Fig. 4.1).

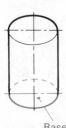

Figure 4.2 A right geometrical solid

Right — a right geometrical solid is one in which the axis passes through the centre of the base and at right angles to the base (Fig. 4.2).

Figure 4.3 Truncated pyramid

Truncated — a truncated solid is one which has had a part removed by a cutting plane passing through the solid at an angle other than a right angle to the axis (Fig. 4.3).

Figure 4.4 Frustum of a solid

Frustum — the frustum of a solid is that part which remains after a piece has been removed by a cutting plane passing through the solid (Fig. 4.4).

Regular — a regular geometrical solid is one in which the base is a regular plane figure.

Apex — the upper point of a cone or of a pyramid is known as that solid's apex. See Fig. 4.1.

50

4.2 Prisms

The true shape of all sections taken through a prism at right angles to its axis will be the same shape and size.

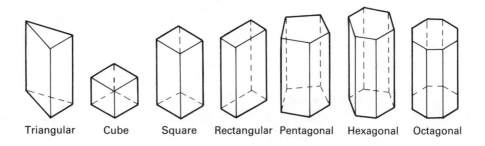

Triangular   Cube   Square   Rectangular   Pentagonal   Hexagonal   Octagonal

Figure 4.5   Prisms

4.3 Pyramids

The true shape of sections taken at right angles to the axis of a pyramid will be the same shape, but will decrease in size, the nearer the cut is taken to the apex of the pyramid.

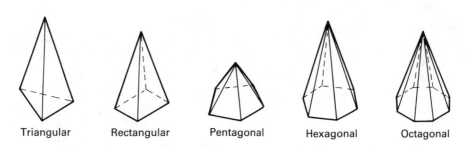

Triangular   Rectangular   Pentagonal   Hexagonal   Octagonal

Figure 4.6   Pyramids

4.4 Cylinders

The true shape of all sections taken at right angles to the axis of a right cylinder will be circles of the same diameter.

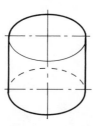

Figure 4.7   A cylinder

4.5 Cones

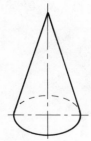

The true shape of sections taken at right angles to the axis of a right cone will be circles which decrease in diameter the nearer the sections are taken to the apex of the cylinder.

Figure 4.8 A cone

4.6 Spheres

The true shapes of all sections taken at any angle through a sphere are circles. All sectional cuts taken through the centre of a sphere result in great circles of sphere diameter.

Figure 4.9 A sphere

4.7 Worked Examples

Worked Example 4.1

A plan and the outline of the front view of a truncated regular hexagonal prism is given in Fig. 4.10. Complete the front view and add an end view as seen in the direction of the arrow E.

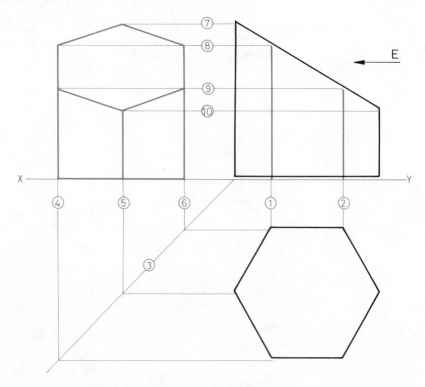

Figure 4.10 Worked Example 4.1

Solution 4.1

> Draw an XY line;
> Project 1 and 2 from the plan;
> Complete the front view;
> Draw 3 at 45° to XY;
> Project 4, 5 and 6 from the plan via 3;
> Project 7, 8, 9 and 10 from the front view;
> Complete the end view.

Worked Example 4.2

Complete the projection of an equilateral triangular prism, Fig. 4.11, by adding a plan as seen from P and an end elevation as seen from E. One edge of the prism rests on a flat plane XY. An **auxiliary** view of the prism is included.

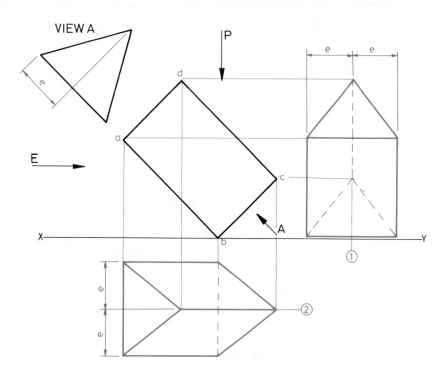

Figure 4.11   Worked Example 4.2

Solution 4.2

> Draw 1 at right angles to XY;
> Draw 2 parallel to XY;
> Project a, b, c and d across 1 and 2;
> Measure e (half of triangle base) across each side of 1 and 2;
> Complete the two views;
> Add hidden detail.

Worked Example 4.3

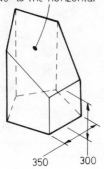

This face slopes at 45° to the horizontal

350   300

Figure 4.12

Fig. 4.12 shows a truncated pentagonal prism. To scale 1:5 construct a plan, a front elevation and an end elevation.

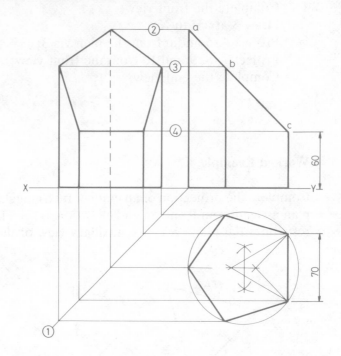

Figure 4.13   Worked Example 4.3

Solution 4.3

Draw the plan (see Section 2.5);
Project into the front elevation;
Draw 1 at 45° to XY;
Project part of the end elevation via 1;
Project 2, 3 and 4 from a, b and c;
Complete the end view.

Worked Example 4.4

Add a plan to the given view, Fig. 4.14, of a truncated square pyramid and an end view as seen from B. Add an auxiliary plan as seen from AP.

Solution 4.4

Project to obtain the square of the plan;
Draw the diagonals of the square;
Project a and b into the plan;
Complete the plan;
Project the end view of the complete pyramid;
Project a and b into the end view;

Complete the end view;
Project 1, 2, 3, 4 and 5 at right angles to ab;
Mark off cd (base edge length) and then e and f;
Mark g — the apex of the pyramid;
Complete the auxiliary plan.

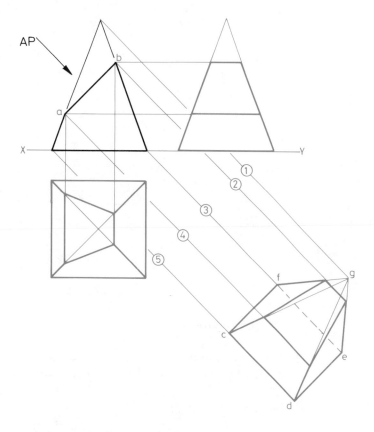

Figure 4.14   Worked Example 4.4

Worked Example 4.5

The plan, apex (A) and cutting plant S-S of a truncated hexagonal pyramid are given in Fig. 4.15, drawn on a square grid. Complete the plan and the front view and add an end view to the right of the front view.

Solution 4.5

Complete the front view;
Project the end view of the complete pyramid;
Project a, b, c and d from the front view to the end view;
Complete the end view;
Draw the diagonals of the plan;
Project from a, b, c and d into the plan;
Complete the plan.

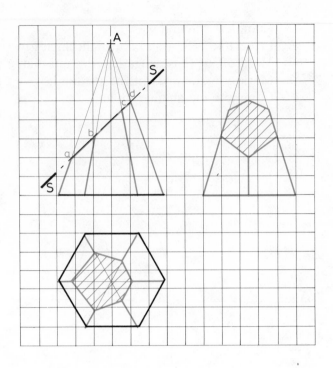

Figure 4.15 Worked Example 4.5

Worked Example 4.6

Fig. 4.16 is a pictorial view of a triangular pyramid in which all faces are triangles with all edges 60 mm long. Construct a front view, a plan and an end view of the solid.

Solution 4.6

Draw the plan — an equilateral triangle with edges 60 mm long (Section 2.3).

   Project vertically from a, b and c;
   Set a compass to 60 mm;
   From d strike an arc on to 1 to give e, the apex of the pyramid;
   Complete the front view;
   Project from the front view and plan to obtain the end view.

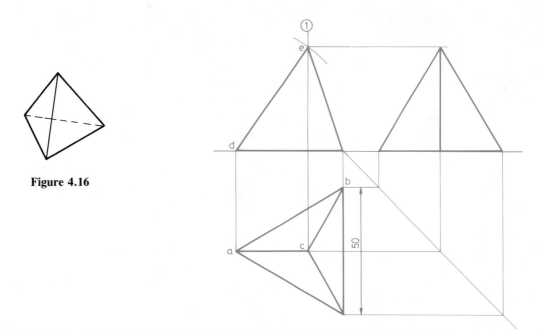

Figure 4.16

Figure 4.17   Worked Example 4.6

Worked Example 4.7

The front elevation of a truncated cylinder is given in Fig. 4.18.

    (a) Add a plan and an end elevation (Solution 4.7(a)).

    (b) Add an auxiliary plan as seen in the direction of the arrow Z (Solution 4.7(b)).

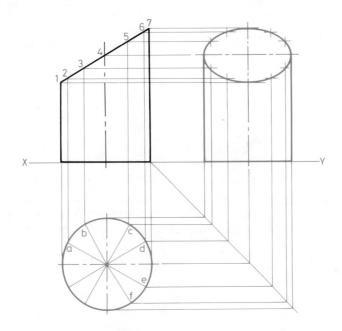

Figure 4.18   Worked Example 4.7(a)

Draw the plan;
Divide the plan circle into 12 equal parts (30°, 60° set square);
Project a, b, c and d into the front view;
Project c, d, e and f into the end view;
Project 1, 2, 3, 4, 5, 6 and 7 into the end view;
Complete the end view.

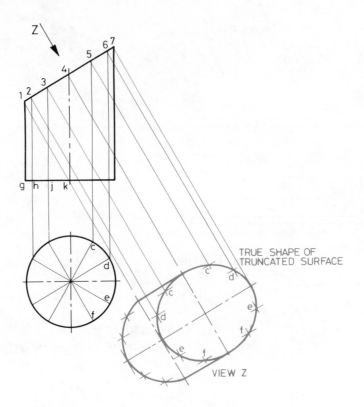

Figure 4.19 Worked Example 4.7(b)

Solution 4.7(b)

Project from 1, 2, 3, 4, 5, 6 and 7 at right angles;
Draw a centre line at right angles to the projection lines;
With a compass transfer the lengths de, cf and the circle diameter of the auxiliary plan;
Complete the **true shape** of the truncated surface.
The base of the cylinder is projected into the auxiliary plan using a similar method.

Worked Example 4.8

A stand to hold a medal prize is made from a plastic in the form of a truncated cylinder with a recess cut into one end. A front elevation of the stand is given in Fig. 4.20. Add a plan to the drawing.

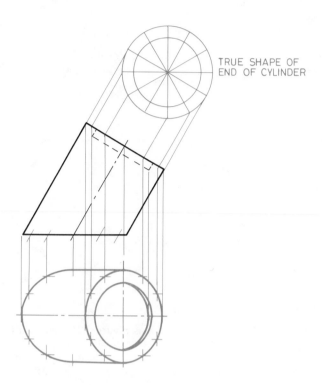

TRUE SHAPE OF
END OF CYLINDER

Figure 4.20   Worked Example 4.8

Solution 4.8

Draw the **true shape** circle of the cylinder;
Divide this circle into 12 equal parts;
Project the 12 points into the front view;
Construct the plan of the base (see Worked Example 4.7);
Construct the plan of the top (see Worked Example 4.7);
Add the ellipse of the top.

Worked Example 4.9

The front view of a truncated cone is given in Fig. 4.21. Construct an end view and a plan.

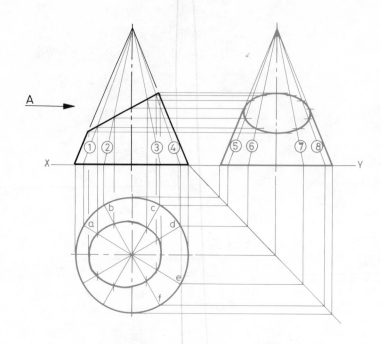

Figure 4.21   Worked Example 4.9

Solution 4.9

Draw the plan of the complete cylinder;
Divide into 12 equal parts;
Project from a, b, c and d into the front view;
Draw 1, 2, 3 and 4;
Project from the plan and front view to obtain the end view of the complete cone;
Project c, d, e and f into the end view;
Draw 5, 6, 7 and 8;
Project points from the slope line of the front view into the end view;
Complete the end view;
Project points from the slope line into the plan;
Complete the plan.

Worked Example 4.10

A cone rests on a flat surface XY as shown by its front view, Fig. 4.22. Add a plan.

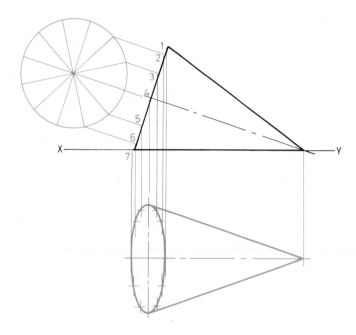

Figure 4.22   Worked Example 4.10

Solution 4.10

Project the circle of the cone base;
Divide into 12 equal parts;
Project back to the given front view to obtain 1, 2, 3, 4, 5, 6 and 7;
Draw the centre lines of the plan;
Construct the ellipse of the plan base (see Worked Example 4.7(b));
Construct the plan.

Worked Example 4.11

Three touching spheres of different diameters are shown in the given front view, Fig. 4.23. Add a plan.

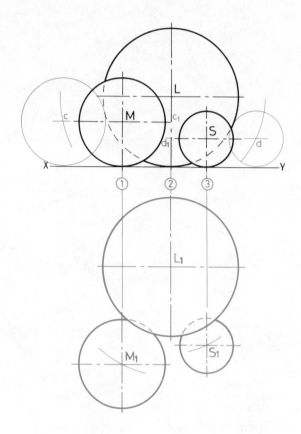

Figure 4.23 Worked Example 4.11

Solution 4.11

Project 1, 2 and 3 into the plan;
Draw the plan of the sphere L in any suitable position;
Set a compass to the sum of the radii of the spheres L and M;
With the compass locate c;
Set a compass to the sum of the radii of the spheres L and S;
With the compass locate d;
Set a compass to cc_1 and, centred at L_1, locate M_1;
Repeat with dd_1 to locate S_1;
The plan of the spheres M_1 and S_1 can now be drawn.

Worked Example 4.12

The drawings, Fig. 4.24, show pictorial details of five bathroom containers.

Complete scale 1:1, in THIRD ANGLE PROJECTION, the incomplete Front and End Views of the five containers arranged, as shown in the given Plan, on a shelf (Fig. 3.43)

Do not include hidden detail.

Do not add colour.

(ULSEB)

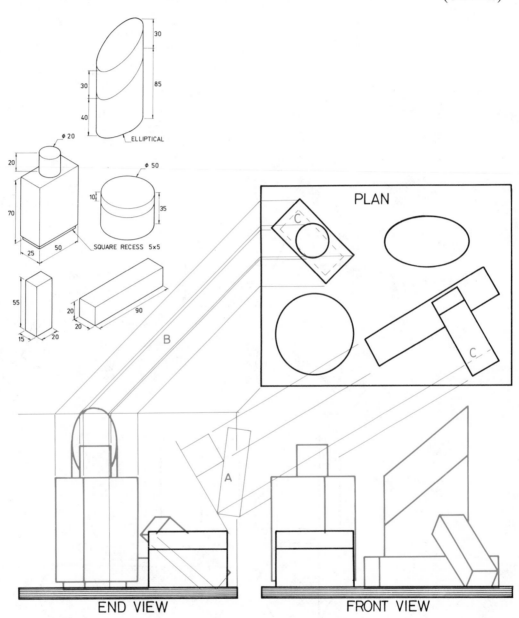

Figure 4.24 Worked Example 4.12

Solution 4.12

The projections of the Front and End Views require considerable care, remembering that the solution is asked for in Third Angle projection.

The Front View was projected from the given Plan, with all heights being measured from the dimensions given in Fig. 4.24. The auxiliary projection (**A**), in construction lines, was necessary in order to obtain the heights of parts of the sloping prism in the Front view.

Projections from the Plan into the End View were made with the assistance of lines at 45° (lines **B**). Heights in the End View were projected from the Front View.

Although hidden detail was not asked for, it became necessary to add some in order to be able to project parts of the given Plan (lines **C**).

4.8 Exercises

4.1
(Fig. 4.25)

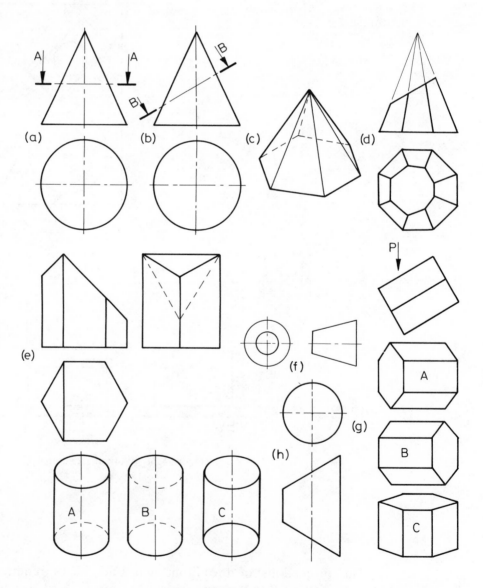

Figure 4.25 Exercise 4.1

(a) Two views of a cone are given. Name the true shape of the surface cut by the Section plane A-A.

(b) Two views of a cone are given. Name the true shape of the surface cut by the Section plane B-B.

(c) Fully name this geometrical solid.

(d) Fully name this geometrical solid.

(e) In which angle of projection are the three given views?

(f) What does the symbol mean?

(g) A front view of a geometrical solid is given. Which plan as seen from P is correct?

(h) A front view of a truncated cylinder drawn in Third angle projection is given. Which is a correct end view — A, B, or C?

4.2

Draw an end elevation of the tilted vase shown in Fig. 4.26 in first or third angle projection. Do not show hidden detail. Complete the projection symbol.

(*SREB*)

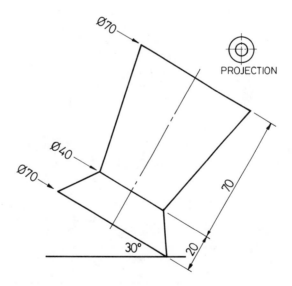

Figure 4.26 Exercise 4.2

4.3

Complete the auxiliary view of the letter E (Fig. 4.27) looking in the direction of the arrow A.

(*LREB*)

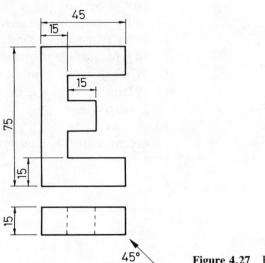

Figure 4.27 Exercise 4.3

4.4

A plan and incomplete front elevation of a lantern are given (Fig. 4.28). Circular holes, the same size as the one shown through the front face, are cut through the other four faces.

Complete the elevation. Hidden detail is not required. Ignore the thickness of the material.

(*SEG Specimen Question*)

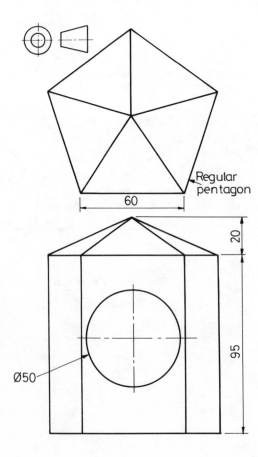

Figure 4.28 Exercise 4.4

4.5

The front elevation of a telescope, circular in section, on a tripod stand is given in Fig. 4.29, together with the plan of the tripod stand on its own, in first angle projection.

(a) Complete the plan.
Show the major and minor axes of the ellipses.
The ellipses may be drawn freehand or with templates.
(b) Draw an auxiliary plan in the direction of arrow A.

(SEG Specimen Question)

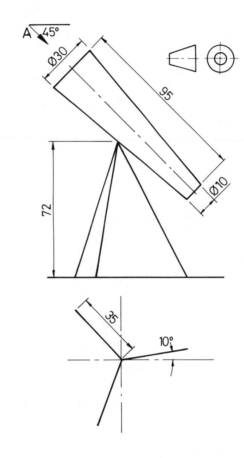

Figure 4.29 Exercise 4.5

4.6

The drawing Fig. 4.30 shows a pictorial view of some building site items.

The orthographic views show plan and incomplete side and end views of the items.

Complete, SCALE 1:10, in THIRD ANGLE PROJECTION the side and end views of the items.

Do not add hidden detail, colour or shading to your drawing.

Sizes of items:

PLANK   1500 long × 400 × 100 mm
LARGE DRUM   600 mm dia × 700 long
SMALL DRUM   350 mm dia × 700 long

(ULSEB)

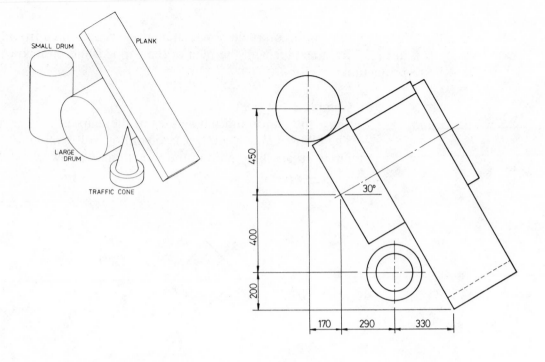

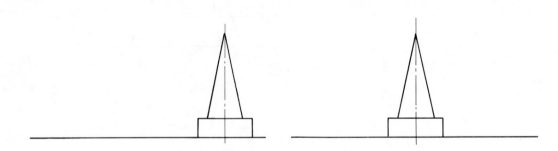

Figure 4.30   Exercise 4.6

Have You Observed the Following Drawing Procedures?

1. Commence by adding a base line **XY** — there is no need to label it in an answer.
2. Project between views with the aid of a line drawn at 45° to XY.
3. Most examination questions in geometrical solid geometry are set, and should be answered in First Angle projection (see Section 3.2).
4. Use **thin** lines for **all** constructions.
5. Do **not** erase constructions.
6. Use **dense black** lines for drawing outlines of your answers.
7. Always consider whether it is best to commence by drawing a **plan**.
8. There is no need to add figures, letters or dimensions to your answers unless the question asks you to so so.
9. Add **centre lines** through the centres of all circles and circular parts.

5 True Lengths, Curves of Intersection and The Helix

5.1 To Find the True Length of a Line and its Angle to the Horizontal Plane

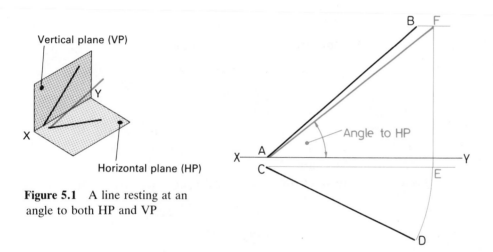

Figure 5.1 A line resting at an angle to both HP and VP

Figure 5.2 To find the true length of a line and its angle to the HP

Draw a line through B parallel to XY;
Draw a line through C parallel to XY;
With a compass centred at C and with radius CD draw the arc DE;
Draw EF at right angles to XY;
AF is the **true length** of the line AB;
The angle **FAY** is the **true angle** between line AB and the horizontal plane XY.

5.2 To Find the True Length of a Line and its Angle to the Vertical Plane

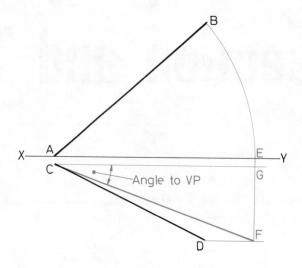

Figure 5.3 To find the true length of a line and its angle to the VP

Draw a line through C parallel to XY;
Draw a line through D parallel to XY;
With a compass centred at A and with radius AB draw the arc BE;
Draw EF at right angles to XY;
CF is the **true length** of the line AB;
The angle **GCD** is the **true angle** between line AB and the vertical plane XY.

5.3 Curves of Intersection — Cylinder to Cylinder

When two cylinders of equal diameter intersect, the front views show the intersections as straight lines (Fig. 5.4). Three First Angle projections of intersecting cylinders of equal diameter are shown — the **curves of intersection** are in red.

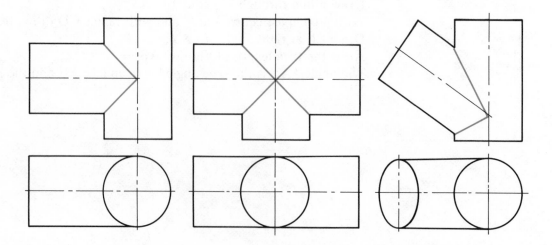

Figure 5.4 Curves of intersection between equal diameter cylinders

70

When cylinders of different diameters intersect, the lines of intersection are curved (Figs 5.5 and 5.6).

5.4 Curves of Intersection — Cylinders with Axes at Right Angles

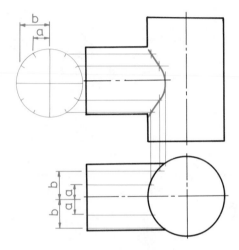

Figure 5.5 Curves of intersection between cylinders of different diameters

Draw the circle of smaller cylinder diameter on its centre line in the front view;

Divide this circle into 12 equal parts;

Measure the lengths **a** and **b** each side of the centre line through the plan;

Project from these points to give 1, 2 and 3 on the plan circle;

Where lines projected from the 12 points on the small circle meet lines projected from points 1, 2 and 3 are points on the curve of intersection;

Draw a curve through these plotted points.

5.5 Curves of Intersection — Cylinders with Axes at an Angle Other than a Right Angle

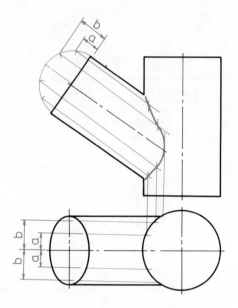

Figure 5.6 Curves of intersection — axes at an angle other than a right angle

The method of finding the curve of intersection follows the same procedure as when the axes meet at right angles.

5.6 Curves of Intersection — Cylinder to Cone

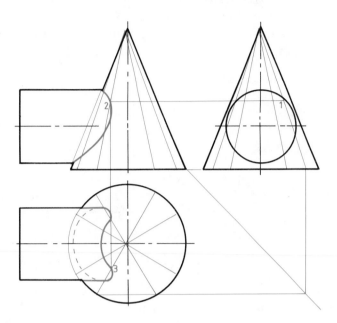

Figure 5.7 Curve of intersection between cylinder and cone

Draw a front view, an end view and a plan of the two solids, without their curve of intersection;

Divide the cone plan circle into 12;

Project the 12 points into the front and end views;

Draw diagonals through the 12 points in the plan;

Join the points to the apex of the cone in front and end views;

Follow the sequence (1) to (2) to (3) to plot points on the curve of intersection in the front view and in the plan;

Repeat this sequence for other points on the required curve.

5.7 Construction of a Helix

A helix is the **locus** of a point moving in a straight line on the surface of a cylinder and parallel to its axis as the cylinder rotates. The **helix** is an important curve because of its many applications in screws of all types. Note the term **pitch**. The pitch of a helix is the length of one complete revolution of the curve.

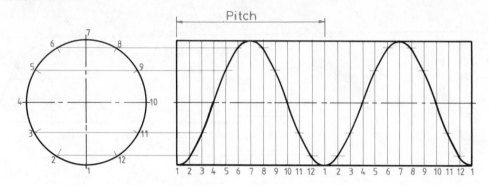

Figure 5.8 Construction of a helix

Divide the circle of the end view into 12;
Divide the pitch length of the helix into 12;
Project from the divisions on the end view to the divisions on the front view;
Draw a curve through the points so obtained.

Note: In the constructions shown in this chapter, it is frequently necessary to divide a circle into 12 equal parts. This can be carried out either with the aid of a 30°, 60° set square or with the aid of a compass set to the circle radius. See Fig. 5.9.

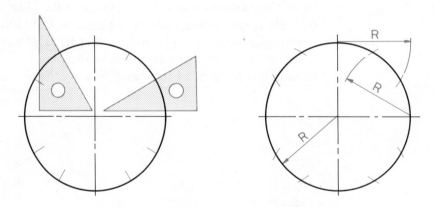

Figure 5.9 Dividing a circle into 12 equal parts

5.8 Worked Examples

Worked Example 5.1

Find the true length of the edge AB of the given square pyramid, Fig. 5.10.

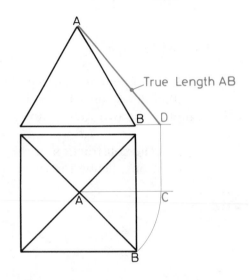

Figure 5.10 Worked Example 5.1

Solution 5.1

> With a compass centred at A in the plan, draw arc BC;
> Draw a line vertically through C;
> AD is the required true length.

Worked Example 5.2

A square pipe is joined to a cylindrical pipe. An incomplete orthographic projection of the jointed pipes is given, Fig. 5.11. Complete the drawing by adding the curve of intersection between the two pipes.

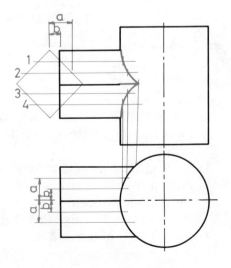

Figure 5.11 Worked Example 5.2

Draw the horizontal lines 1, 2, 3 and 4;
Set a compass to **a** and **b** in turn and transfer these two lengths into the plan;
Draw horizontal lines through a and b in the plan;
Project between the two sets of lines so obtained to find plot on the curve of intersection.

Worked Example 5.3

Fig. 5.12 is a plan of a tap handle. Its outline is based upon a regular pentagon.
    Outline lines for a front view and plan of the handle are given (Fig. 5.13)
Complete the two views, showing all your constructions for:

(a) The construction of the outline of the plan;
(b) Constructing the curves of intersection in the front view.

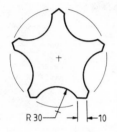

Figure 5.12

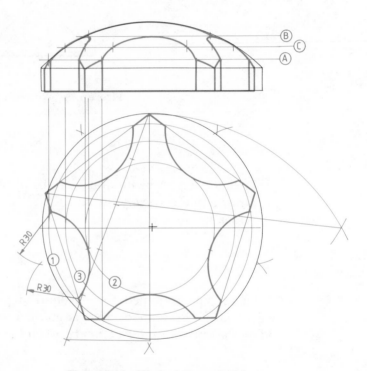

Figure 5.13   Worked Example 5.3

1. Construct the regular pentagon of the plan. (Section 2.5.)
2. Construct the centres of and draw the 30 mm arcs in the plan. Complete the plan.
3. Draw circle 1 passing through the ends of the 30 mm arcs in the plan.
4. Project from 1 to give line A in the front view.
5. Draw circle 2 touching the four 30 mm arcs in the plan.
6. Project from 2 to give line B in the front view.
7. Draw line C about mid-way between lines A and B.
8. Project line C into the plan to give circle 3.

9. Where circle 3 crosses the 30 mm arcs project back to line C to give points on the required curves of intersection.
10. Complete the curves of intersection.

Note: Only one circle (3) and its projected line C have been drawn for the construction of the curves of intersection. In practice it would be advisable to draw more such lines to achieve greater accuracy. Only one circle and line have been used here for the sake of clarity in showing the method of constructing the curves of intersection.

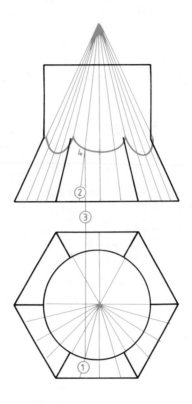

Figure 5.14   Worked Example 5.4

Worked Example 5.4

A stand consists of a cylinder let into a regular hexagonal pyramid. Part of the front elevation and plan of the stand are given (Fig. 5.14). Complete the two views by adding the curves of intersection between the two solids.

Solution 5.4

1. Draw the lines of the complete pyramid in both front view and plan.
2. Follow the procedure given by the lines 1, 2, 3 and the plot point 4 to give points on the curves of intersection.
3. Repeat a number of times to give sufficient points through which the curves of intersection can be drawn.

Worked Example 5.5

A helical compression spring made from 4 mm diameter spring steel wire is to be inserted between two bosses as indicated in the full-size drawing, Fig. 5.15. The spring is to consist of 4 pitches. Construct a front view of the centre line through the spring on the given drawing.

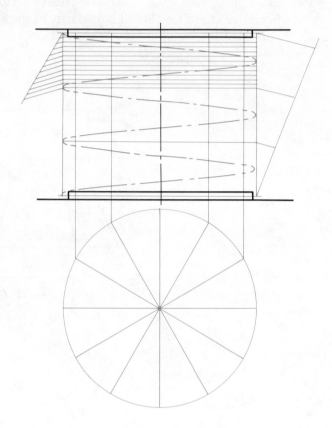

Figure 5.15   Worked Example 5.5

Solution 5.5

1. The question asks for the centre line of the diameter 4 mm steel wire of the spring. The solution must take account of this.
2. The bosses are 4 mm high. The 3 pitches are therefore from the centre of the height of the bosses and 2 mm outside them.
3. Divide the total centre line length into 3.
4. Divide one of these pitch lengths into 12.
5. Divide the plan circle into 12.
6. Construct one helix (see Section 5.4).
7. Copy this helix on to the other two pitches with the aid of tracing paper.

5.9 Exercises

5.1
(Fig. 5.16)

    (a) Draw the end view of the two joined wires AB and BC.
    (b) Find the true length of each of the two wires.

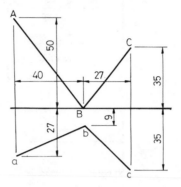

Figure 5.16 Exercise 5.1

5.2
The given drawing, Fig. 5.17, is a front elevation and plan of a truncated hexagonal pyramid. Find the true length of one sloping edge of the solid.

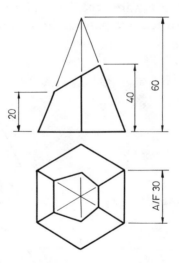

Figure 5.17 Exercise 5.2

5.3

Two hexagonal pipes intersect as shown in the given incomplete 3-view projection, Fig. 5.18. Complete the projection by adding the lines of intersection between the two pipes.

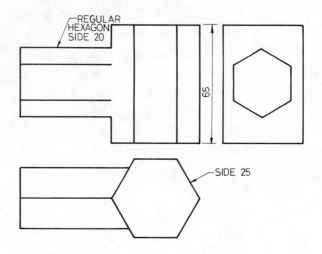

Figure 5.18   Exercise 5.3

5.4

A slide for a children's playground is to be made in the shape of a conical helix as indicated by the outline front view and plan of Fig. 5.19. Each of the three pitches of the slide are to be of equal length even though their diameters will increase towards the base of the slide. Add to given two views a correctly constructed line passing through the centre of the slide.

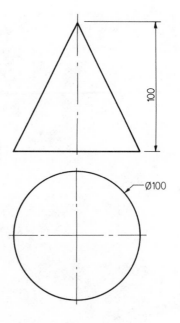

Figure 5.19   Exercise 5.4

5.5

A pictorial sketch and two end views of the outline for part of a steel roof structure are shown in Fig. 5.20.

(i) Draw, to the same scale as the given views and in the direction of arrow Z, the end elevation of the roof structure.

(ii) Obtain, graphically, the true lengths of members AB, BC and CD. Measure these lengths then complete the table.

(Scottish)

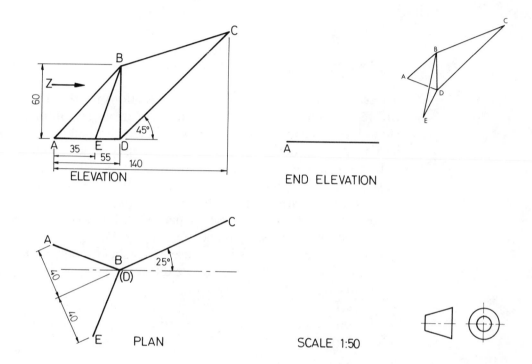

Figure 5.20 Exercise 5.5

Have You Observed the Following Drawing Procedures?

1. Learn how to find a **true length** of a sloping line in any position. The use of true length constructions is of particular importance when constructing surface developments, described in Chapter 6.
2. When finding the angle at which a line is sloping, view the line at right angles and project what is seen.
3. When constructing a curve of intersection, take several parallel imaginary section lines through one view of the object. Then project from where the section lines cut parts of that view on to other views.
4. When constructing a 'curve' of intersection between two solids with the same sectional shape, the result will be a line sloping at 45° between the two parts.
5. Commence drawing helical curves by dividing the circular view into 12 parts.

6 Surface Development

6.1 Introduction

(a) Syllabuses for GCSE Technical and Graphic Communication Examinations

These require a knowledge of the constructions for the surface developments of prisms, pyramids, cylinders and cones. A further requirement is that candidates should be able to apply this knowledge to the making of models and to the surface development of items such as are used in packaging.

In the examples of developments which are included in this chapter, gluing tabs will not be included other than in the first item in Section 6.2. Gluing tabs are, of course, necessary when a development is being constructed for the purpose of making articles from paper or card, but when articles are to be made from other materials such as sheet metals or sheet plastics, no gluing or jointing tabs may be needed. This is because many sheet metal or sheet plastics articles are jointed by soldering, brazing, welding or with a variety of adhesives, in which the joints are made edge to edge.

If a surface development is being constructed to be used as a template, to be placed on sheet material and then drawn around, the development may be referred to as a pattern.

Notes:
1. When constructing surface developments, particular care must be taken to ensure that true lengths of all lines are correctly constructed. Failure to see to this detail will result in incorrect constructions.
2. In all the constructions included in this chapter, developments will be shown shaded.

6.2 Surface Development of a Packet

The majority of packets such as those made for the packaging of foodstuffs, take the form of rectangular prisms. Such a packet is shown in Fig. 6.1. The surface development for the card from which the packet is to be made is shown in Fig. 6.2. Note the gluing and tucking-in-tabs, included in Fig. 6.2 — these being the areas in the drawing which have not been shaded.

Further examples of the developments of the surfaces of prisms will be given in the Worked Examples later in the chapter.

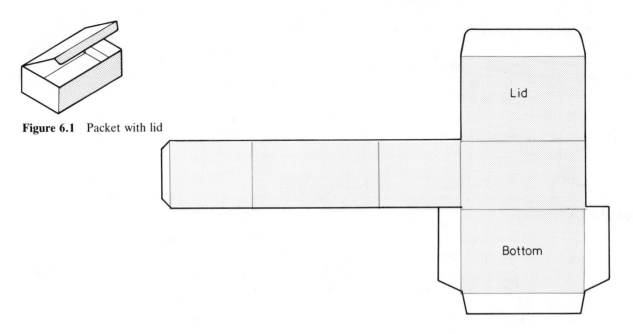

Figure 6.1 Packet with lid

Figure 6.2 Surface development of a packet

6.3 Surface Development of a Pyramid

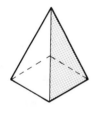

Figure 6.3 A pyramid

Fig. 6.3 shows a square pyramid on which a surface development is required. Proceed as follows:

1. Draw a front view and a plan of the pyramid — Fig. 6.4.
2. Find the **true length** (TL) of one sloping edge of the pyramid. See Section 5.3.
3. Set a compass to TL and draw an arc.
4. Set a compass to the base edge length AB.
5. With the compass mark off 4 divisions along the arc of radius TL.
6. Join the points so found as shown in Fig. 6.5.
7. Add a development of the base — a square of edge length AB.

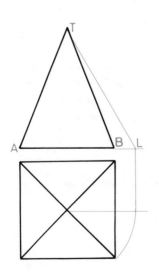

Figure 6.4 Front view and plan of square pyramid

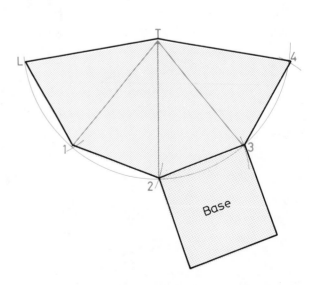

Figure 6.5 Surface development of square pyramid

83

6.4 Surface Development of a Cylinder

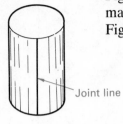

Figure 6.6 A cylinder

Fig. 6.6 shows a cylinder made from sheet material. The joint line for the material is indicated. To construct its surface development proceed as shown in Fig. 6.8:

1. Draw a front view and plan of the cylinder — Fig. 6.7.
2. Divide the plan circle into 12 equal parts.
3. Draw a rectangle of cylinder height and of a length equal to 12 of the equal spaces of the circle of the plan.
4. Add the base and top of the cylinder.

Note: An alternative method for finding the length of the rectangle is to multiply the radius of the plan circle by 2π and to make the rectangle $2 \times \pi \times R$. For example, if the circle is of a radius of 30 mm, the rectangle length would be: $2 \times 3.14 \times 30 = 188.4$ mm

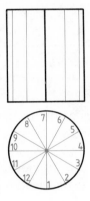

Figure 6.7 Front view and plan of cylinder

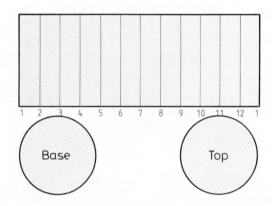

Figure 6.8 Surface development of cylinder

84

6.5   Surface Development of a Cone

Fig. 6.9 shows a cone to be made from sheet material. The joint line of the material is indicated on the drawing.

To construct a surface development for the cone proceed as indicated in Fig. 6.11:

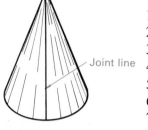

Figure 6.9   A cone

1. Draw a front view and a plan of the cone — Fig. 6.10.
2. Divide the plan circle into 12 equal parts.
3. Set a compass to the slant height TL of the front view.
4. Draw an arc of radius TL.
5. Set a compass to one of the 12 equal divisions of the plan circle.
6. With the compass so set step off 12 divisions along the arc of radius TL.
7. Complete the development as shown in Fig. 6.11.
8. Add the base — a circle of cone base diameter.

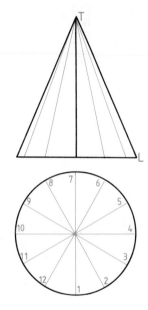

Figure 6.10   Front view and plan of cone

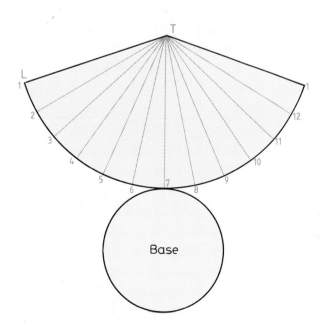

Figure 6.11   Surface development of cone

85

6.6 Worked Examples

Worked Example 6.1

Figure 6.12

Fig. 6.12 is a pictorial drawing of a hexagonal box made from cardboard. A front view and plan of the box are given in Fig. 6.13.

Construct a development for the sides and top of the block. Your answer should include the letter **E**.

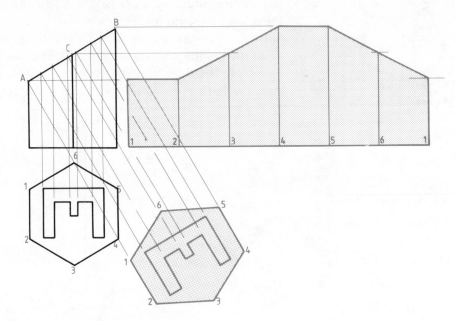

Figure 6.13 Worked Example 6.1   **Figure 6.14** Solution 6.1

Solution 6.1

1. Mark off 6 divisions of base edge length along a straight line level with the base of the front view.
2. Draw the verticals 1 to 6 to 1.
3. Project from A, B and C to cross these verticals.
4. Draw the development of the upright parts as shown.
5. Project lines from A, B and C at right angles.
6. Draw the true shape of the prism top as shown.
7. The letter E is projected from the plan on to the line AB in the front view and then at right angles on to the true shape surface.

Worked Example 6.2

A sheet metal tray in which letters waiting for posting can be placed is shown in Fig. 6.15.
Construct a scale 1:2 development of the tray.

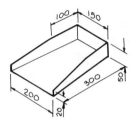

Figure 6.15

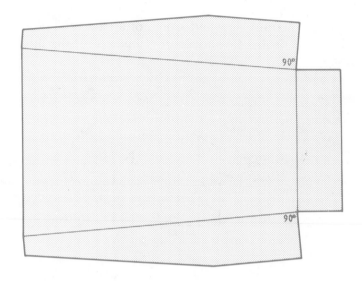

Figure 6.16 Worked Example 6.2

Solution 6.2

See Section 6.3

Worked Example 6.3

Fig. 6.17 shows a cardboard container to hold a single videotape.

(a) Draw with instruments a scale 1:2 development of the container. Your development should include the tabs for gluing the container together.
(b) Draw **freehand** to an approximate scale 1:5 a development of a cardboard box designed to hold six of the videotape containers.

Figure 6.17

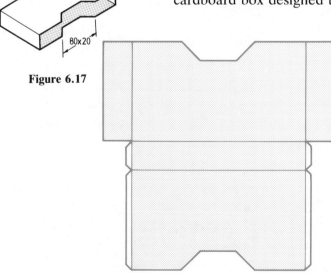

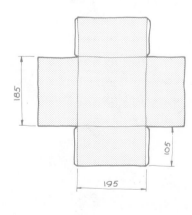

Figure 6.18 Worked Example 6.3(a)

Figure 6.19 Worked Example 6.3(b)

See Section 6.2 for both solutions.

Worked Example 6.4

A front view and a plan of a truncated pentagonal prism is given in Fig. 6.20. Construct a surface development of the upright sides of the prism.

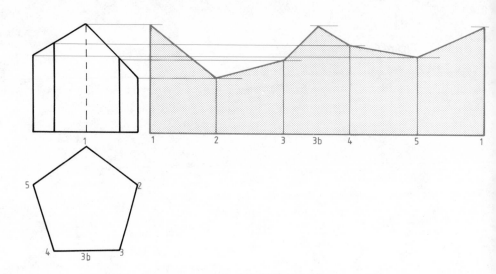

Figure 6.20   Worked Example 6.4   **Figure 6.21**   Solution 6.4

The method of solving this problem follows closely the solution to Worked Example 6.1 above.

Worked Example 6.5

Sketch, **freehand** and approximately full size, the development of a regular hexagonal pyramid of base edge length 30 mm and of height 80 mm.

Solution 6.5

Figure 6.22   Worked Example 6.5

Fig. 6.22. See also Section 6.4.

Worked Example 6.6

Fig. 6.23 is a front view of a lampshade which is part of a right cone. Construct a surface development of the shade.

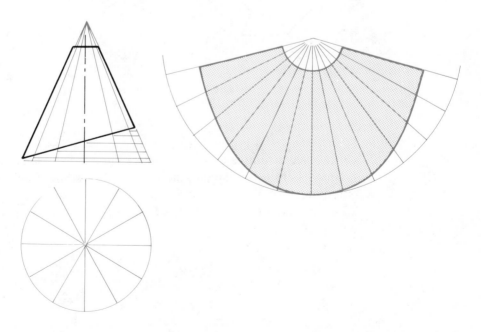

Figure 6.23   Worked Example 6.6   **Figure 6.24**   Solution 6.6

The method of solving this problem follows the same procedures as given in Worked Example 6.9 above.

Worked Example 6.7

The sketch (Fig. 6.25) shows a restaurant lampshade. Orthographic views of the lampshade are given in Fig. 6.36.

    (i) Draw a development of Part A of the shade.
    (ii) Draw a development of Part B of the shade.

(Welsh)

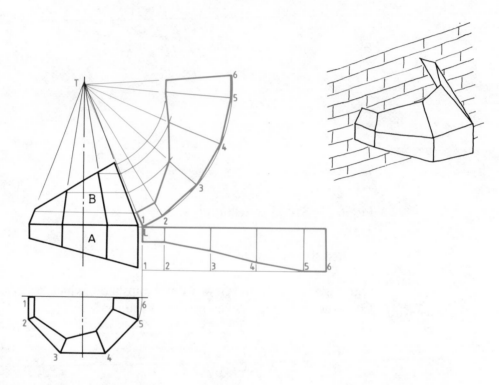

Figure 6.25   Worked Example 6.7   **Figure 6.26**   Solution 6.7

Solution 6.7

This is an example of a development in which a true length of an edge had to be found before the development of Part B could commence. The line **TL** is the required true length. See Section 6.3.

    The development of Part A follows the construction methods given in Worked Example 6.1.

Worked Example 6.8

The pictorial view, Fig. 6.27, shows a disposable cup with an applied five pointed star.

When seen in side view the star appears to be regular with the points touching the given circle.

    (a) Construct the star within the given circle.
    (b) Construct the development of the applied star.
         Do not add colour.

(ULSEB)

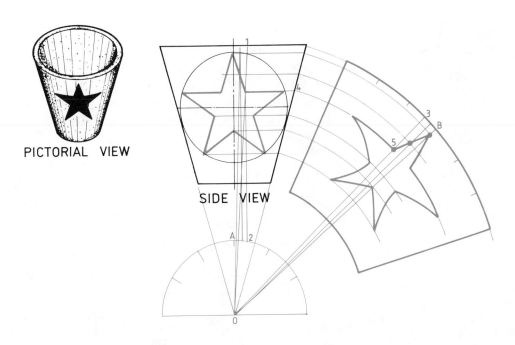

PICTORIAL VIEW

SIDE VIEW

Figure 6.27   Worked Example 6.8   **Figure 6.28**   Solution 6.8

Solution 6.8

Worked Example 6.8 is a typical **structured** question, in which the solution becomes progressively more difficult. When answering this form of question, answer as much of it as you can, because marks will be available for each part of the structure. The question is in three parts:

    1. Constructing the star in a circle — easy;
    2. Beginning the development — harder;
    3. Constructing the development of the star — difficult.

Construct star — Section 2.5.

    Although not asked for, it is helpful to construct the development of the frustum of the cone — Section 6.5.

    A number of points must now be constructed to obtain the development of the star. Only the construction of three such points is shown — to avoid crowding the given solution with construction lines. For each constructed point, follow the procedure 1 to 5:

1. Draw O1 through the required point on the star;
2. Project 1 into the plan circle to give 2;
3. Transfer the distance A2 to give B3 on the development;
4. Project from the point on the star to 4;
5. Draw arc O4 to meet O3 at 5 — the required point on the star development;
6. Repeat 1 to 5 for as many points as needed.

6.7   Exercises

6.1

Fig. 6.29 is a small-scale First Angle projection of a frame tent.

Working to the same scale, construct the separate developments of the tent fabric for the front, one end and the roof of the tent.

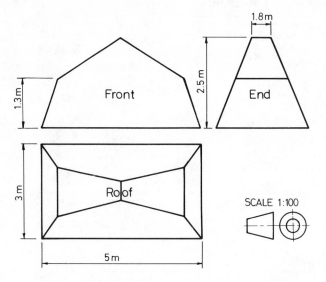

Figure 6.29   Exercise 6.1

6.2

Fig. 6.30 is a front view and a plan of a cardboard model of a water tower required as part of a geography project.

Construct a development of each of the two parts of the model. The roof and base of the upper part of the development can be ignored.

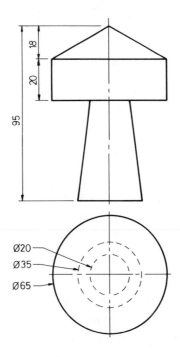

Figure 6.30   Exercise 6.2

6.3

Fig. 6.31 is a two-view orthographic projection of a stand, designed to hold a trophy. The stand is to be made from sheet metal. No base is required.

Construct developments of the two parts required for the stand, working to the same scale as the given views.

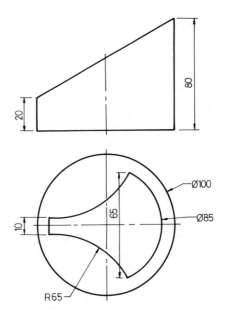

Figure 6.31   Exercise 6.3

Fig. 6.32 is a front view of a cowling for an air vent to be fitted to a factory roof. The cowling is part of a right cone.

Construct a development of the part shown in the given front view.

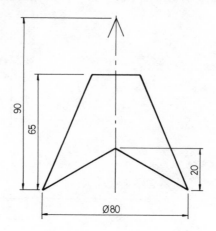

Figure 6.32   Exercise 6.4

6.5

The sketch, Fig. 6.33, shows a rubbish bin which could be fixed to a wall. It is made from thin sheet steel. Three orthographic views are also given in Fig. 6.37. The front view is incomplete.

(a) Complete the front view.
(b) Construct the development of surface A.
Do not include the back in your development.

(*SREB*)

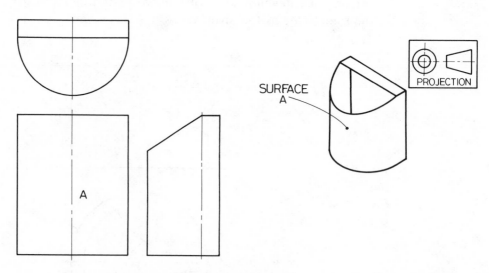

Figure 6.33   Exercise 6.5

6.6

The drawing (Fig. 6.34) shows a pictorial view of a TOY BOAT which is made from thin sheet material.

Draw FULL SIZE a development of the toy including the top and base. Ignore the thickness of the material and do not add joining tabs.

Corner **A** is given for you in the space provided.

(ULSEB)

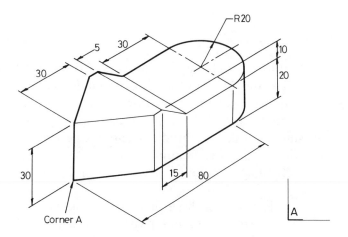

Figure 6.34   Exercise 6.6

Have You Observed the Following Drawing Procedures?

1. Development construction methods **must** be based on true lengths. Check that your method does give accurate true lengths.
2. Some questions which include developments can require many construction lines. To avoid confusion, number parts of the construction so that it is quite sure which construction lines on a drawing refer to which part of the development.
3. Unless asked for, do not include gluing tabs in your answers.
4. Some questions ask for part developments. You will be wasting valuable time in an examination if you give a full development when only a part one is necessary.
5. A knowledge of development constructions is frequently required when preparing models for projects.

7 Shading and Colouring

7.1 Introduction

Methods of adding shading and/or colouring to drawings should be used when those studying for Graphic Communication examinations are compiling sheets of graphics for their projects or course work (see Chapter 14). Questions requiring a knowledge of shading and/or colouring are set in GCSE examinations in the subject. Take coloured pens and/or pencils into the examination room with you when sitting the examination.

Shading or colour is included in graphics to:

1. Create a three-dimensional appearance;
2. Provide a greater visual impact;
3. Draw attention to parts of a drawing.

7.2 Colouring Media

Shading and colour can be added to drawings with pencils (both black and colour), pens, water colour washes, marker pens, or by adding dry transfer tones.

Pencils — For shading with black pencils, light shades can best be achieved with pencils of H or HB grade. To obtain darker shades, use B or BB grades. If using colour pencils, it is best to avoid using the wax type of pencil 'crayon', because these leave an oily, waxy finish to the colour, not well suited to this form of graphics.

Pens — A variety of colour pens suitable for adding colour to drawings, are available in many shops at the present time. Colour **Biro** pens, pens of the **Penstik** types, **Technical** pens which can be filled with coloured inks, are examples of the type of colour pen available. When selecting a **throw-away** colour pen, choose one in which the colour solvent is a spirit, to allow for quick drying of the colour.

Water colour wash — is best applied with a good quality brush. Water colours sold in tubes are usually of a better quality that those sold in block form.

Marker pens — are available in a huge range of colours with both wide and fine tips or nibs. Those in which the colour is spirit-based are best, because then the colour dries very quickly when it has been applied.

(a) When Using Colour

- *Primary* colours are — red, blue, yellow.
- *Secondary* colours are mixtures of primary colours;
  Red + blue = purples and mauves;
  Red + yellow = oranges;
  Yellow + blue = greens.

- White can be added to give pastel pinks, blues, greens, yellow, etc.
- Blues and greens are said to be *cold* colours.
- Reds and oranges are said to be *warm* colours.
- Reds and their secondary colours *contrast* with blues and their secondary colours.
- Colours with similar mixture of primary colours *complement* each other.

7.3 Thick-line Outlining

One of the most commonly used methods of attempting to create a 3-D appearance is by making some of the lines in a drawing much thicker than others. Fig. 7.1 shows a box, drawn in two-point estimated perspective with all its outer lines drawn several times as thick as inner lines.

7.4 Pencil Shading

Figs 7.2–7.8 are examples of shading using either black or colour pencils:

Fig. 7.2 — One-tone shading with an HB pencil.
Fig. 7.3 — Two-tone shading — HB and B pencils.
Fig. 7.4 — Two-tone shading with HB and B pencils, but with no outline of the drawing.
Fig. 7.5 — One-tone shading using a colour pencil. Outline of the box has been drawn with an ink pen.
Fig. 7.6 — Two-tone colour pencil shading. Box outline drawn in ink.
Fig. 7.7 — Two-tone colour pencil shading with box outlined in thick ink lines.
Fig. 7.8 — Two-tone colour pencil shading with no outline to the drawing.

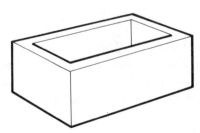

Figure 7.1 Thick-line outlining

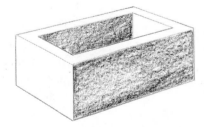

Figure 7.2 One-tone shading — HB pencil

Figure 7.3 Two-tone shading — B and HB pencils

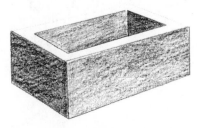

Figure 7.4 Two-tone shading with no outline — B and HB pencils

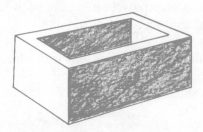

Figure 7.5 One-tone shading with outline in ink — colour pencil

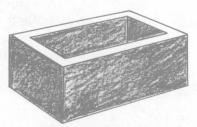

Figure 7.6 Two-tone shading with ink outline — colour pencil

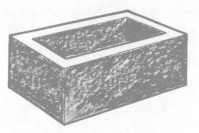

Figure 7.7 Two-tone shading with thick-line outline — colour pencil

Figure 7.8 Two-tone shading with no outlines — colour pencil

7.5 Dry Transfer Tone Shading

Dry transfer tones — A number of firms make sheets of dry transfer tones, the best known being **Letraset**. A large range of different tones is available. Rather expensive, but well worth the cost for some types of graphics.

Figs 7.9–7.11 show the stages in shading a drawing using dry transfer tones.

(a) Stage 1 — Fig. 7.9

1. Draw the outline of the drawing.
2. Choose sheets of dry transfer of suitable tones.
3. With a sharp scalpel knife cut out from the first sheet a piece of tone of a size a little larger than is required to cover the area to be toned.
4. Lightly rub the piece in position on the drawing.

(b) Stage 2 — Fig. 7.10

1. With the sharp knife carefully cut through the piece of tone along the lines it is to occupy on the drawing.
2. Peel off the surplus tone.
3. Rub the tone firmly on to the drawing. A purpose-made burnishing tool is best for this purpose.

(c) Stage 3 — Fig. 7.11

Add other tones as needed to complete the shading.

Note: The firms who make the dry transfer tones supply them in a large range of different types of shading and in different depths of each shade. Fig. 7.12 shows six of the more commonly used tones from this large range. The terms such as **10% dot** mean that the actual dots making up the tone occupy 10% of the area of the sheet. This percentage figure is, of course, an indication of the depth of shading possible with that tone.

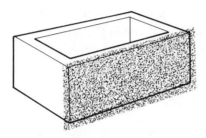

Figure 7.9 Dry transfer shading — Stage 1

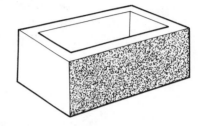

Figure 7.10 Dry transfer shading — Stage 2

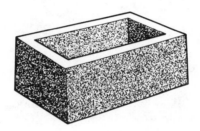

Figure 7.11 Dry transfer shading — Stage 3

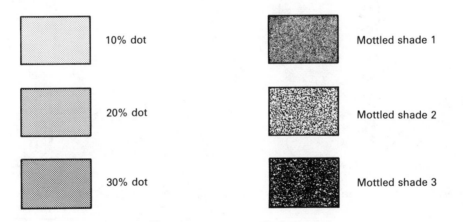

Figure 7.12 Six common dry transfer shades

7.6 Shading Curved Surfaces

Figs 7.13–7.15 show three different methods of shading to give a 3-D appearance to drawings which include curved surfaces.

(a) Shading with Black Pencil — Fig. 7.13

The depth of shading increases towards the outer part of the curve. Shading commenced on the outer part of the cylinder using a grade B pencil, changing to a grade HB pencil towards the middle of the curve.

(b) Straight Line Shading of a Curve — Fig. 7.14

Thin lines have been drawn vertically along the drawing of the cylinders at varying distances apart — closer together towards the outside, widening towards the middle.

(c) Curved Line Shading of a Curve — Fig. 7.15

Curved lines, broken at intervals, have been drawn with equal spacing across the cylinders.

Note: There are other methods of shading curved surfaces. The three given are simple to apply and give the student ample choice for this purpose.

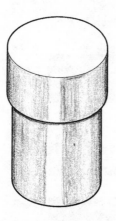

Figure 7.13 Curved surface shading — B and HB pencils

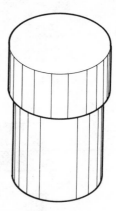

Figure 7.14 Curves surface shading — straight lines

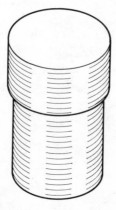

Figure 7.15 Curved surface shading — curved lines

7.7 Geometrical Method of Drawing Shadows

It should be noted that this method has no strict basis in geometry. Proceed as follows:

1. Draw the object to which a shadow is to be added — in this example, a two-point estimated perspective drawing of a cube.
2. Select a point **LS** as the light source. The position of **LS** depends upon where you wish the shadow to appear.
3. Select the point **G** — which is assumed to be on the same surface on which the cube has been placed. **G** must be vertically below **LS**.
4. From **LS** draw lines through the corners **A, B, C** and **D**.
5. From **G** draw lines through **A, B, C** and **D**.
6. Where these pairs of lines meet are points at the corners of the required shadow.
7. Draw and shade the shadow areas as shown.

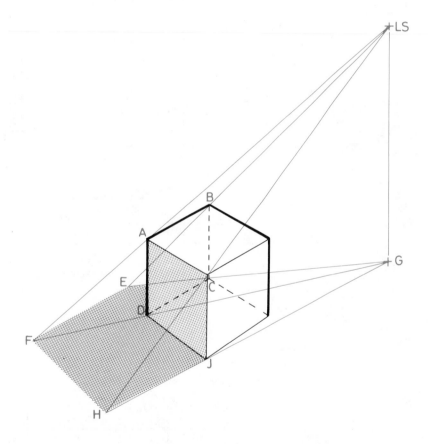

Figure 7.16 Geometrical method of drawing shadows

101

7.8   Water-colour Washes

Figs 7.17 and 7.18 are examples of colour washes added to emphasise part of each drawing. Rules for applying colour wash are:

1. Mix up enough colour to complete the work in hand.
2. A more even colour is obtained if the surface being coloured is first wetted by brushing with clean water.
3. As the colour is applied, keep the **working edge** wet, by working from one side to the other or from top to bottom of the area being coloured.
4. Do not over-load the brush with colour.

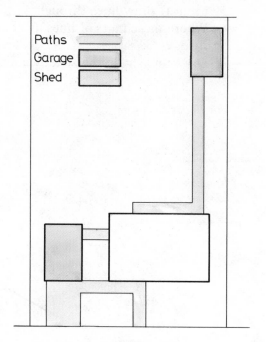

Figure 7.17   An example of colour wash

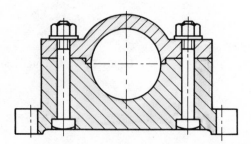

Figure 7.18   An example of colour wash

7.9 Marker Colouring

Fig. 7.19 is an example of a drawing which has been outlined with thick lines and has been coloured with markers to produce a 3-D appearance. Two shades of marker were used and the internal edges have been highlighted with white water colour added with a thin brush. A white colour pencil could have been used to highlight these edges.

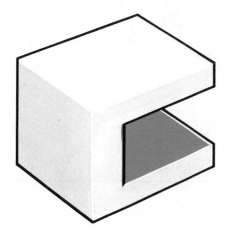

Figure 7.19   An example of marker pen colouring

7.10 Worked Examples

Worked Example 7.1

Shade the given circle (Fig. 7.20) to make it appear as a sphere.

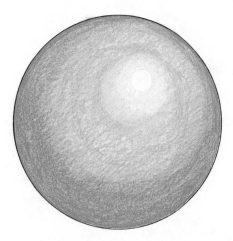

Figure 7.20   Worked Example 7.1

Solution 7.1

A small area has been selected on the circle as if light was shining on that area of the sphere. From this area the shading becomes darker towards the outline of the circle (the sphere outline).

A colour pencil was used to shade the drawing.

Worked Example 7.2

Add a shadow to the given drawing. Fig. 7.21, as if light is falling on the object from behind and to the left.

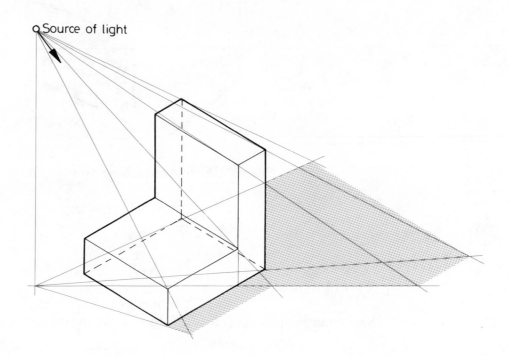

Figure 7.21   Worked Example 7.2

Solution 7.2

The geometrical method (Section 7.7) was used in the answer to this example. Shadow was added with dry transfer tone.

Worked Example 7.3

Shade the given drawing to produce a three-dimensional effect.

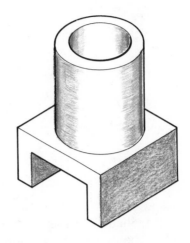

Figure 7.22   Worked Example 7.3

Solution 7.3

See Sections 7.3 and 7.6 above. Shading has been added using colour pencils.

7.11   Exercises

7.1

(a) Fig. 7.23. Carefully colour each area of the sports wristband. If you do not have the colour print its name in the relevant area. Do not use the same colour twice.
Circle A — primary colour.
Area B   — secondary colour.
Area C   — warm colour.
Area D   — cold colour.
Area E/F — a pair of contrasting colours.
Area G   — A complimentary colour to the circle colour.

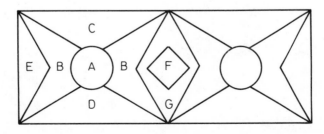

Figure 7.23   Exercise 7.1(a)

(b) Shade the cube, Fig. 7.24, as if light is coming from in front, below and to the right of it.

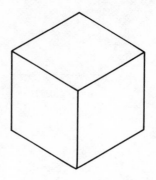

Figure 7.24 Exercise 7.1(b)

(c) Shade the hemisphere, Fig. 7.25, as if the light source is above and behind your left shoulder.

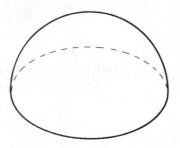

Figure 7.25 Exercise 7.1(c)

(*SREB*)

7.2

(a) Fig. 7.26. Carefully colour red only those lines which would need to be drawn heavier to improve the visual clarity.

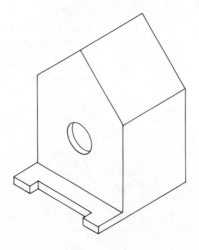

Figure 7.26 Exercise 7.2(a)

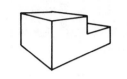

(b) Certain construction lines have been omitted from Fig. 7.27.
Provide and label the following:
   (i) both vanishing points
   (ii) the eye level line
   (iii) tick the only line that is a true length
   (iv) this type of drawing is a ....

Figure 7.27 Exercise 7.2(b)

(*SREB*)

Have You Observed the Following Drawing Procedures?

1. In Graphic Communication you normally have a choice of either adding colour or shading, or not adding it.
2. Colour or shading can be applied to your drawings to emphasise outlines, to emphasise shape, to give your 2-D drawings a 3-D appearance, or to create a greater visual impact.
3. In Graphic Communication, colour is usually added with colour pencils, crayons or colour wash. Colour pens and marker pens may also be of value in some work.
4. Unless you are colour shading a drawing, shading is best applied with grade HB, B or BB pencils.
5. Do not add colour or shading to a drawing unless its graphic effect is increased by the addition. Do not get into the habit of applying colour or shading to all your drawings. Many items of graphics do not need colour to carry the graphic message they have been drawn to communicate.
6. Dry transfer tints are an effective means of shading drawings, but can be expensive.
7. Colour and shading are of good value when preparing sheets of drawings for projects or course work — see Chapter 14.
8. Reds and mixtures of colours between red and yellow tend to give a warm effect. Blues and mixtures of colours between blue and yellow tend to give a cold effect.
9. Greys and off-whites make good background colours against which other parts of a drawing will stand out.
10. Dark colours tend to make a drawing look heavy.
11. Pastel colours tend to give a drawing an appearance of lightness.

Note: Examples of coloured drawings will be found in Chapters 8, 14 and 15.

8 Technical Illustration

8.1 Introduction

All GCSE Technical Communication and Graphic Communication syllabuses require a knowledge of the following methods of pictorial drawing:

1. Isometric drawing
2. Cabinet drawing
3. Planometric drawing
4. One-point and two-point **estimated** perspective
5. Freehand drawing — often referred to as **sketching**

8.2 Exploded Drawings

A further requirement of the syllabuses is that candidates should be able to show a knowledge of **exploded** pictorial drawing. Exploded drawings can be produced using any of the above pictorial methods. In examinations at GCSE level candidates are usually only required to produce exploded **isometric** drawings. However, an understanding of exploded drawings produced by other methods may occasionally be needed — e.g. by such exploded drawings being included on an examination paper as part of a question.

Note: All the GCSE syllabuses for the subject state that aids may be used by candidates when producing pictorial drawings. **Ellipse templates** are of particular value for this purpose. **French curves** and **Flexicurves** can be useful when drawing curves which are not elliptical in pictorial drawings.

8.3 Isometric Drawing

Isometric drawing is the most commonly used Graphic Communication method among those used for producing pictorial drawings with the aid of instruments.

Commence any isometric drawing by constructing a rectangular prism of length (**L**), width (**W**) and height (**H**) into which the article to be drawn could be tightly fitted. All the lines of this construction 'box' are drawn by angles of either 30° or 90° to the horizontal. Within the framework of this box, details of the article can be constructed.

Note: All measurements on an isometric drawing **must** be taken along either a 30° line or a 90° line. Thus, if any detail in an isometric drawing is at an angle which is not parallel with the length, width or height of the original framework, measurements for that detail **must** be taken along either a 30° or a vertical line. This rule applies to all sloping surfaces and all curved surfaces.

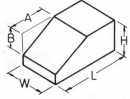

Figure 8.1 An isometric drawing of a block

8.4 Constructing an Isometric Drawing

To construct the isometric drawing shown in Fig. 8.1 proceed as follows:

1. Draw a vertical line of length **H**
2. Draw the two 30° lines of lengths **L** and **W** (Fig. 8.2).
3. Complete the construction box as shown in Fig. 8.3.
4. Measure the lengths **A** and **B** along the 30° and 90° lines — Fig. 8.4.
5. Complete the isometric drawing — Fig. 8.5.

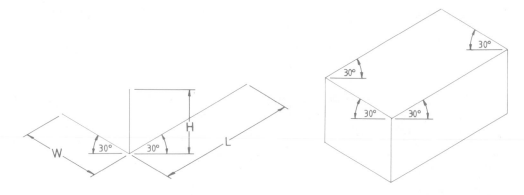

Figure 8.2   Isometric drawing — stage 1   **Figure 8.3**   Isometric drawing — stage 2

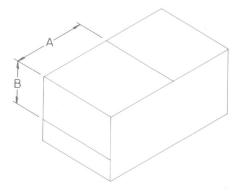

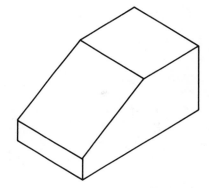

Figure 8.4   Isometric drawing — stage 3   **Figure 8.5**   Isometric drawing — stage 4

8.5 An Isometric Drawing Including Circular Parts

Circular parts within an isometric drawing can be drawn either freehand or with the aid of an isometric ellipse template. Fig. 8.6 is an isometric drawing of a block in which a hole has been bored. Two methods of constructing isometric drawings of this block are shown in Figs 8.7 and 8.8.

(a) Drawing Freehand Isometric Circles (Fig. 8.7)

1. Draw the outline of the isometric drawing of the rectangular prism of the block.
2. Draw part of the circle of hole diameter, add its vertical centre line and then draw several vertical ordinates (lines 1, and 2) across the circle in any suitable positions.

109

3. Copy these ordinates on to the isometric drawing measuring the length of each ordinate on either side of the centre line **AOB**, with the aid of a compass to give the 8 points numbered 1, and 2. Add the vertical centre line **COD**.
4. Draw a freehand curve through these plotted points.

(b) Drawing Isometric Circles with the Aid of an Ellipse Template (Fig. 8.8)

1. Draw the outline of the isometric drawing of the rectangular prism of the block.
2. Draw construction lines at 30° and 60° through the position of the centre of the hole.
3. Place the required size ellipse of an ellipse template over these two lines and draw the required ellipse.

Note: The ellipse of the back of the hole in the isometric drawings is plotted and drawn in a similar manner.

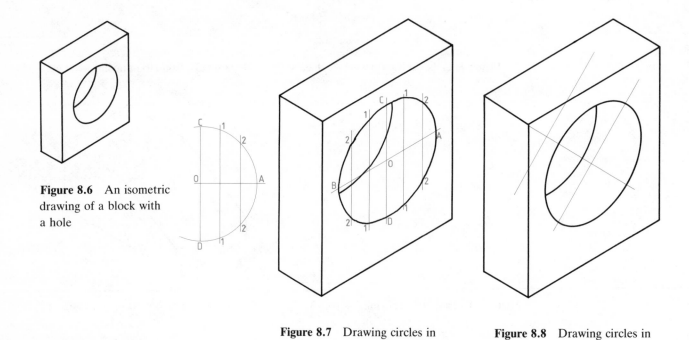

Figure 8.6 An isometric drawing of a block with a hole

Figure 8.7 Drawing circles in isometric — freehand

Figure 8.8 Drawing circles in isometric — with ellipse aid

8.6 Cabinet Drawing

If an object for which a pictorial drawing is required is of a fairly complicated shape when viewed from any one direction, cabinet drawing can be the preferred method of producing the required drawing. Cabinet drawing may, however, produce pictorial views which look somewhat distorted.

8.7 Constructing a Cabinet Drawing

Fig. 8.9 is a cabinet drawing of a shaped block. To construct this drawing proceed as follows:

Figure 8.9 A cabinet drawing of a block

1. Draw a front view of the block (Fig. 8.10).
2. Draw lines at 45° from selected points on the front view (Fig. 8.11).
3. Mark off half-size measurements along the 45° lines (Fig. 8.12).
4. Complete the drawing as shown (Fig. 8.13).

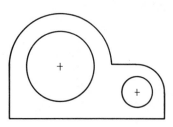

Figure 8.10 Cabinet drawing — stage 1

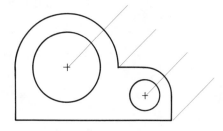

Figure 8.11 Cabinet drawing — stage 2

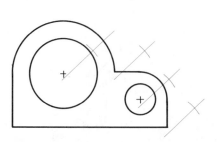

Figure 8.12 Cabinet drawing — stage 3

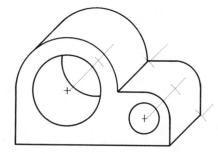

Figure 8.13 Cabinet drawing — stage 4

8.8 Planometric Drawing

Planometric drawings always commence with a drawing of a plan of the item which is to be drawn. This plan is drawn as if resting at 45°/45° or at 30°/60° to the horizontal. Planometric drawing is suitable for constructing pictorial views of rooms, buildings, layouts of streets, display areas and other such fairly large items.

8.9 To Construct a 45°/45° Planometric Drawing

1. Draw the plan of the room (Fig. 8.14).
2. With a 45° set square construct the outlines of the items within the room. The verticals should be drawn about $\frac{3}{4}$ of the scaled heights of the various details (Fig. 8.15).
3. Complete the planometric drawing (Fig. 8.16).

Note: The $\frac{3}{4}$ scaling of the height of each vertical is not critical. Some may prefer a $\frac{2}{3}$ scaling. If full-length lines are drawn, a 45°/45° planometric tends to look as if it has been drawn too high.

Figure 8.14 Planometric drawing — stage 1   **Figure 8.15** Planometric drawing — stage 2

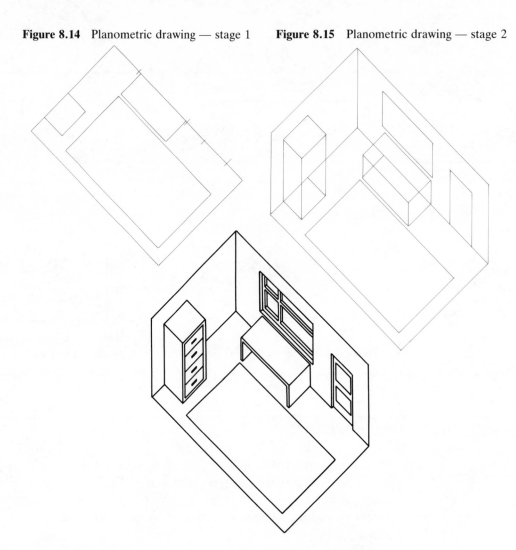

Figure 8.16 Planometric drawing — stage 3

8.10 To Construct a 30°/60° Planometric Drawing

Follow the same procedures as for the 45°/45° example given above (Section 8.9), except that in the case of a 30°/60° degree planometric drawing, there is no need to draw the vertical at a reduced scale.

Fig. 8.17 is an example of a 30°/60° planometric drawing.

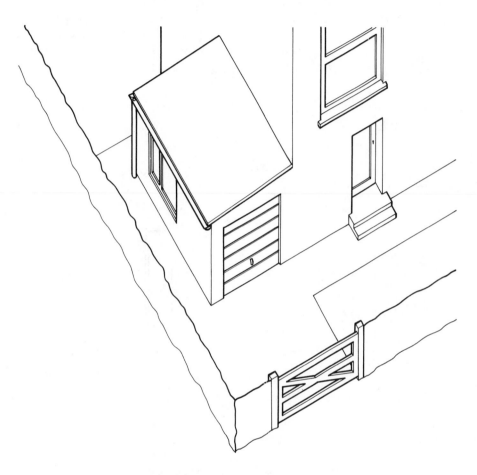

Figure 8.17 A 30°, 60° planometric drawing

8.11 Estimated Perspective Drawing

It is a common experience when looking along a straight length of road or railway track, to see the sides of the road or track appearing to become closer together in the distance. In the far distance the sides of road or track appear to meet. In a perspective drawing this point where the sides apparently meet is called a **vanishing point (VP)**. All methods of perspective drawing are based upon this idea of lines meeting at remote VPs.

GCSE examination syllabuses only require a knowledge of **estimated** perspective drawing — either **one**-point or **two**-point perspective. In estimated perspective, the positions of VPs are guessed at — they are indeed estimated.

Note: Vanishing points (VPs) in perspective drawings are usually positioned on the drawing sheet at a scaled height of an average human being's eyes (about 1.7 metres). In **estimated** perspective, the positions of VPs are normally estimated at points chosen to result in reasonable well-proportioned drawings.

8.12　One-point Estimated Perspective Drawing

Three one-point estimated perspective drawings of a letter **L** are shown in Fig. 8.18. In the three examples the single **VP** is above the letter — either to the right, immediately above, or to the left. To draw each of the three examples the procedure is as follows:

1. Draw a front view of the letter **L**.
2. Select a **VP**.
3. From points on the front view draw lines to the **VP**.
4. Estimate the required depth of the letter.
5. Complete the drawing as shown.

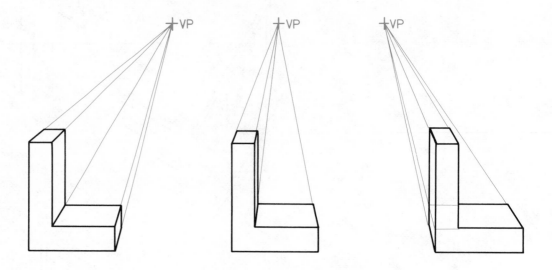

Figure 8.18　Three one-point estimated perspective drawings

8.13　Two-point Estimated Perspective Drawing

Two two-point estimated perspective drawings of a letter **L** are shown in Fig. 8.19. One drawing is as if looked at from above, the second drawn as if looked at from below. To draw each of the two examples, proceed as follows:

1. Select the two VPs. **Note**: they must be on the same horizontal line.
2. Draw the front vertical corner line of the letter **L**.
3. From top and bottom of this line draw lines to the two VPs.
4. Estimate along the lines to the VPs the depth of the letter.
5. Complete the drawings as shown.

Note: The width and depth of drawings in two-point estimated perspective are less than the actual width and depth. This is because of the foreshortening which takes place in all perspective drawing. The length of the width and depth lines are estimated.

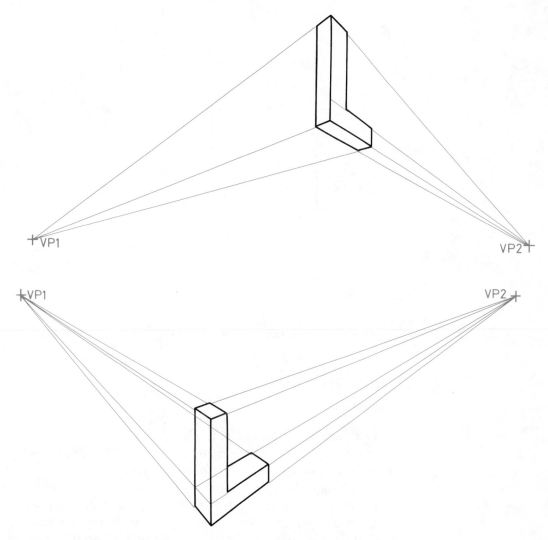

Figure 8.19 Two two-point estimated perspective drawings

8.14 Equal Division in Perspective Drawings (Fig. 8.20)

1. Draw the diagonals of the perspective quadrilateral.
2. Draw vertical line **D**.
3. Draw the diagonals of the smaller quadrilaterals.
4. Draw vertical lines **B** and **F**.
5. Repeat stages 3 and 4 to obtain the positions of the vertical lines **A, C, E** and **G**.

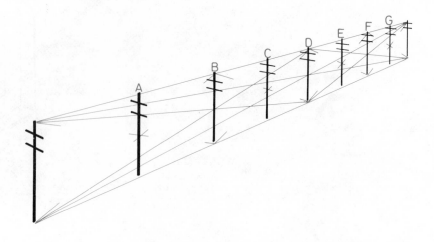

Figure 8.20 Method of construction to obtain equal spacing in estimated perspective drawing

8.15 Freehand Drawing

Pictorial **sketches** based on isometric, cabinet, planometric or perspective methods can be produced freehand, without the aid of instruments, or with only minimal aid from instruments. The advantage of sketching freehand is that the resulting **sketch** can usually be produced more quickly. The main use of freehand **sketching** is in preparation work — to test ideas, to plan layout, to sketch a number of solutions to a problem on paper fairly quickly. Some of the Worked Examples given below include solutions drawn freehand.

When working freehand, pencils of HB or B grades are preferable to the harder 2H or 3H pencils commonly used when drawing with the aid of instruments.

8.16 Drawing on Grid Papers

Papers on which square or isometric grids are printed in green or blue lines can be used to aid the speedy production of orthographic projections, isometric or cabinet drawings — freehand or instrument-aided. Such grid papers are printed with spacing of 5 to 10 mm between the lines. 5 mm grids are those in most common use. Some of the solutions to the worked examples given below are given on grid papers.

8.17 Worked Examples

Worked Example 8.1

The five illustrations of Fig. 8.21 are different forms of drawing method. Selecting your answers from the list below, complete the questions (a) to (e):

Cabinet drawing, isometric drawing, planometric drawing, one-point perspective drawing, two-point perspective drawing, orthographic projection.

(a) **A** is drawn in: PLANOMETRIC DRAWING.
(b) **B** is drawn in: TWO-POINT ESTIMATED PERSPECTIVE.
(c) **C** is drawn in: ONE-POINT ESTIMATED PERSPECTIVE.
(d) **D** is drawn in: ISOMETRIC DRAWING.
(e) **E** is drawn in: CABINET DRAWING.

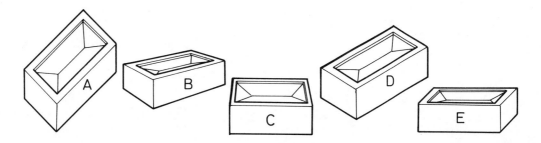

Figure 8.21   Worked Example 8.1

Solution 8.1

This is printed in red above.

   Note: In Figs 8.21 and 8.23 the drawings have been outlined with thicker lines than other lines in the drawings. This outlining technique is explained further in Chapter 7.

Worked Example 8.2

Two small-scale views of a wardrobe and chest of drawers are given — Fig. 8.22. Choosing your own Vanishing Points, construct a **two-point estimated perspective** drawing of the wardrobe and chest of drawers. Work to approximately the scale of the given views.

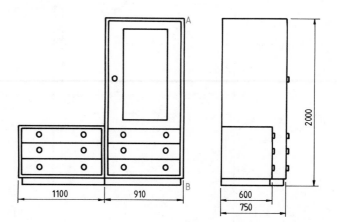

Figure 8.22   Worked Example 8.2

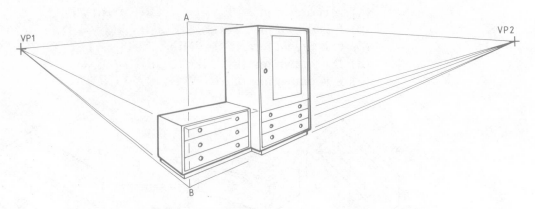

Figure 8.23

Note:

1. Decide on the direction in which the drawing is to be viewed.
2. Height of VPs at 1700 mm above base of wardrobe.
3. Dimensions taken from Fig. 8.22.
4. Commence with nearest vertical corner **AB** at scaled height of 2000 mm.
5. Heights of wardrobe, mirror, etc. taken from line **AB**.
6. Width and depth of both the chest of drawers and the wardrobe reduced from given orthographic drawing. Otherwise the drawing will appear too wide and deep.

Worked Example 8.3

A Third Angle orthographic projection of a box made for holding a number of video tapes is given in Fig. 8.24.

Draw, **scale 1:2**, an isometric drawing of the box.

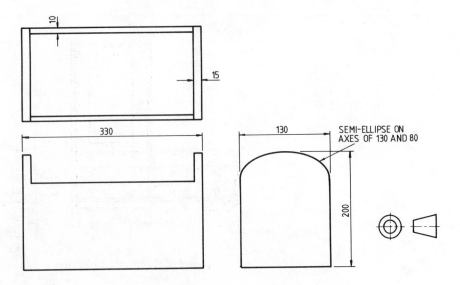

Figure 8.24 Worked Example 8.3

Solution 8.3

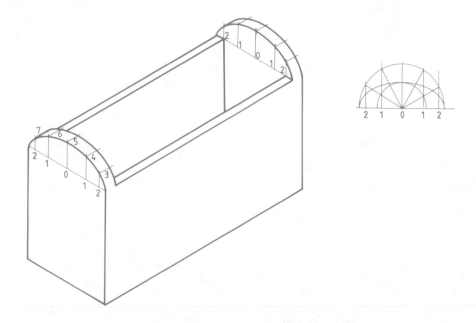

Figure 8.25   Solution 8.3

Although the ends of the box are semi-elliptical, the method as is used for constructing an isometric drawing of a semi-circle is quite suitable for drawing the curves of the box ends in this example.

Note how the isometric curves of the semi-ellipses are repeated on the back edges of the box ends. Lines at 30° are taken from the plotted points for the curve and the end thickness measured along each of them — lines 3 to 7.

Worked Example 8.4

Fig. 8.26 is a two-view orthographic drawing of a timing device to switch lights on and off automatically.

Sketch, **freehand**, a full-size pictorial view of the device.

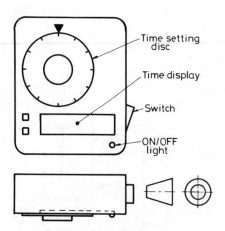

Figure 8.26   Worked Example 8.4

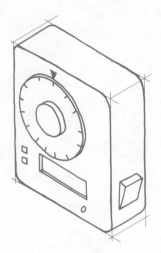

Figure 8.27   Solution 8.4

Note the following three details in this solution:

1. The question does not ask for any particular method of freehand drawing. The chosen method was to make a freehand drawing on isometric lines.
2. A 'box' outline has been drawn with the aid of a 30°, 60° set square, within which the freehand sketch could be constructed.
3. A compass was used to transfer lengths of the various parts of the drawing from the given Fig. 8.26.

Worked Example 8.5

A three-view orthographic projection of coupling is given in Fig. 8.28.

On the given grid (Fig. 8.29), make a full-size **freehand exploded** drawing of Parts 2 and 3 of the coupling.

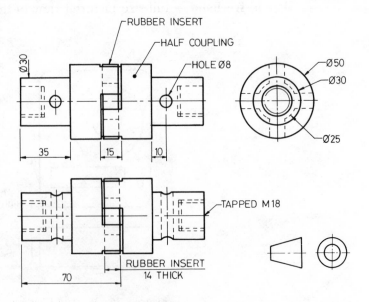

Figure 8.28   Worked Example 8.5

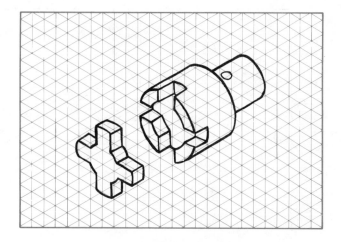

Figure 8.29 Solution 8.5

A difficulty in answering this question was to decide on the best position from which to view the parts of the coupling. If looked at from an end, although details of the tapped hole could have been included in the answer, the more important parts of the coupling — the 'teeth' which engage the rubber insert — could not have been clearly shown.

Worked Example 8.6

Two views of a desk to be fitted into a corner of a room are shown in Fig. 8.30. A start has been made on a 30°, 60° planometric drawing of the corner of the room into which the desk is to be fitted (Fig. 8.31).

Complete the given drawing Fig. 8.31 adding a drawing of the desk in its fitted position. Dimensions not given should be estimated.

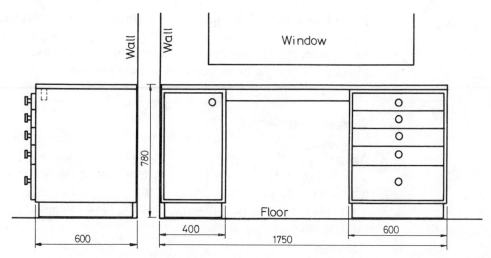

Figure 8.30 Worked Example 8.6

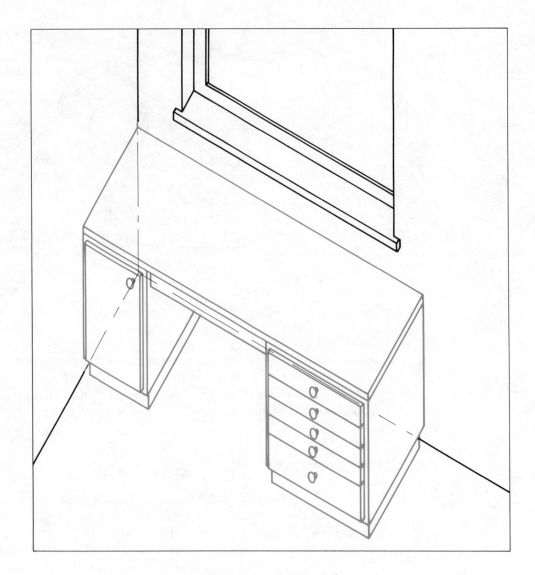

Figure 8.31 Solution 8.6

The solution to this example is a straightforward planometric drawing. By taking measurements from the given starter drawing, the scale worked out as 1:10. Any estimated dimensions had to be in proportion to the remainder of the solution by comparisons between dimensions on the given question drawing.

Worked Example 8.7

An orthographic drawing of a hand voice recorder is shown on a square grid — Fig. 8.32. A start has been made on a two-point estimated perspective drawing of the recorder.

On the given starter drawing, find the two VPs and complete the drawing of the recorder.

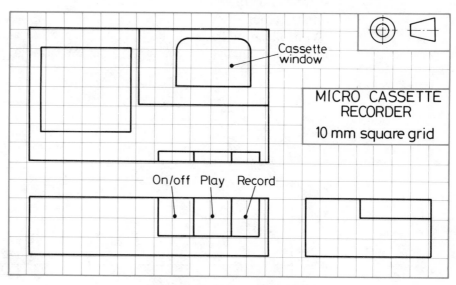

Figure 8.32 Worked Example 8.7

Solution 8.7

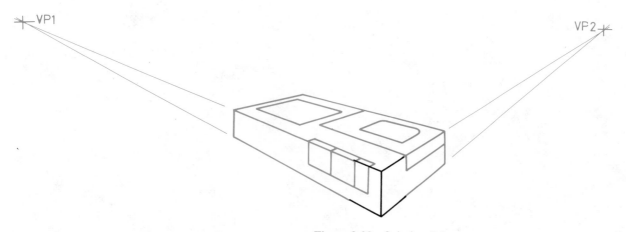

Figure 8.33 Solution 8.7

Lines produced from the starter meet at the two VPs. Check that they are in line horizontally before labelling them as **VP1** and **VP2**. The lengths of the front and side of the recorder in the solution must be estimated — check by trying one or two lengths until the proportions of the drawing look reasonably correct. Remember this is an estimated perspective and correct measurements are not possible.

Worked Example 8.8

The item shown in the orthographic drawing is a solid rubber 'bump stop' from the rear suspension of a car. The manufacturer requires a pictorial illustration for use in a parts catalogue.

Make a suitable pictorial illustration of the bump stop. Your illustration may be freehand, drawn with instruments, or a combination of both and should include colour work.

Your illustration should be in good proportion and approximately twice full size. Measurements may be taken from the orthographic drawing.

(*SEG Specimen Question*)

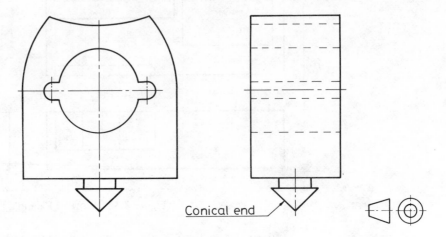

Conical end

Figure 8.34 Worked Example 8.1

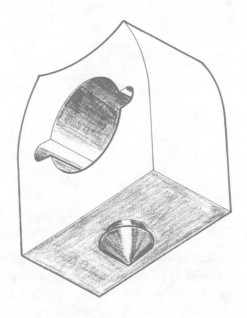

Figure 8.35 Solution 8.1

Solution 8.8

Three techniques were employed in this solution:

1. Thick-line outlining;
2. Pencil shading to produce a background effect;
3. Pencil shading of circular parts and the base.

Note: The view is taken looking up from below in order to show the conical part of the 'bump stop'.

124

8.18 Exercises

8.1

Using instruments, make an isometric drawing of the component shown in Fig. 8.36. Curves must be constructed. (The 4-centre compass arcs method may be used.)

(SREB)

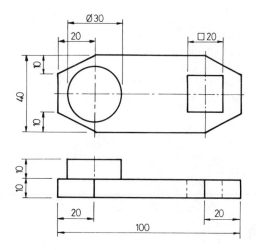

Figure 8.36 Exercise 8.1

8.2

The diagram Fig. 8.37 shows the outline of a timber roof structure. An enlargement of one of the joints has been drawn in plan and elevation.

(i) Draw, to the same scale as the plan and elevation, an end elevation in the direction of arrow X.

(ii) Draw **freehand**, also to the same scale, an isometric sketch of the enlarged joint, within the given box, and with Y at the lowest point.

Omit all hidden detail

(Scottish)

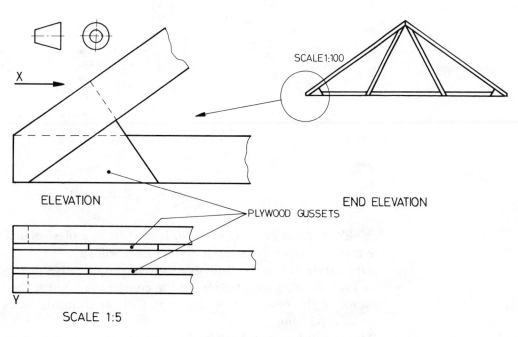

Figure 8.37 Exercise 8.2

8.3

Three views are given (Fig. 8.38) of a spinner used in a table-top 'cricket' game. The numbers 1 and 4 *only* alternate around the spinner. Make a *freehand* sketch of it on the given centre line to about twice the size of the orthographic views. Do not use instruments in your sketch.

(*SREB*)

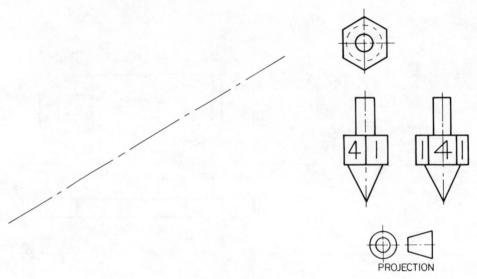

Figure 8.38   Exercise 8.3

8.4

(a) An exploded isometric drawing of a toy engine with a parts list and dimensions is given in Fig. 8.39. Construct a cabinet oblique drawing of the assembled engine with the front visible.

(b) The parts are to be packaged in a box ready for assembly after purchase making economic use of card. Draw full size an elevation and a plan of the parts arranged in the box. Label each part of your drawing.

(*SREB*)

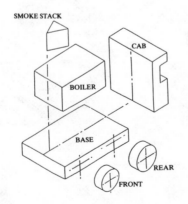

All dimensions in mm.

PART	No	DIMENSION		
		L	W	H
Base	1	90	60	15
Boiler	1	60	40	30
Cab	1	20	60	60
Cut out 10 cm From top			10	20
Front wheels	2	Ø 20 × 10		
Rear wheels	2	Ø 30 × 10		
Smoke stack (Equilateral △)	1	sides 20 height 20		

Figure 8.39   Exercise 8.4

8.5

A child's toy is shown in Fig. 8.40. It consists of a plastics box with four holes in the top into which pegs, each 80 mm long will fit.

Draw **scale 1:2**, using a suitable form of projection, a **pictorial** view of the box in a form suitable for printing on the container in which the toy is to be sold.

Some of the pegs may be drawn in their appropriate holes and others in an exploded position.

Marks will be given for effective use of colour and/or shading.

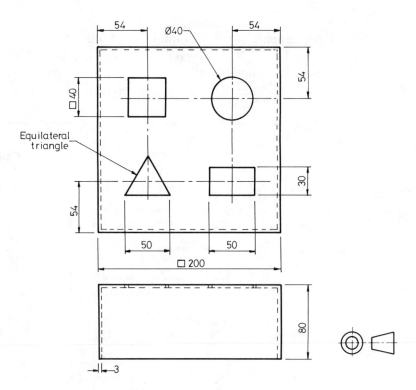

Figure 8.40 Exercise 8.5

8.6

Orthographic views of an empty swimming pool are given in Fig. 8.41 in which the principal dimensions only are shown.

Draw scale 1:100 a planometric 45°/45° degree view of the pool.

Details should be shown simply with the posts, rails and steps of the diving platform indicated by single lines.

Marks will be given for the effective use of colour and/or shading.

(ULSEB)

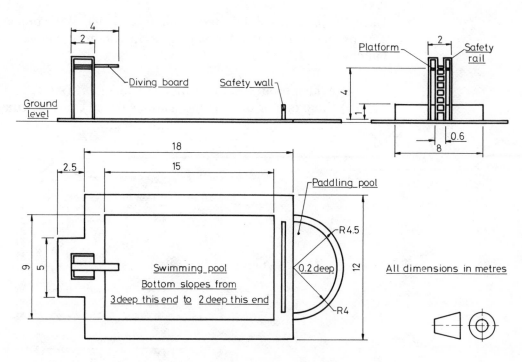

Figure 8.41 Exercise 8.6

127

8.7

Orthographic views of a lathe tool holder are given in Fig. 8.42.

SKETCH FREEHAND a full-size EXPLODED PICTORIAL view of the tool holder showing its assembly in a form suitable for a manual.

Note that the M8 stud in the top of the tool holder is not removable.

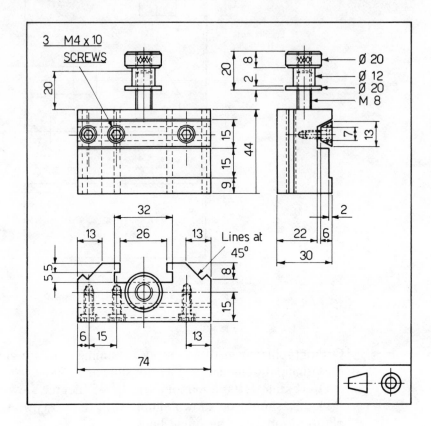

Figure 8.42 Exercise 8.7

8.8

Using the plan (Fig. 8.43), draw a pictorial sketch of the bungalow and garage as seen by an observer at a reasonable distance in front, above and to the left of the building.

(a) Which room has two windows? ....

(b) State one of the missing features which could be considered important

....

(SREB)

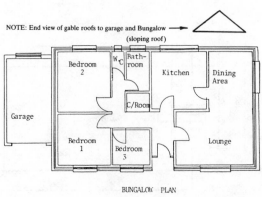

Figure 8.43 Exercise 8.8

Have Your Observed the Following Drawing Procedures?

1. In Graphic Communication the choice of pictorial drawing is between: isometric, cabinet, planometric, estimated perspective (one-point or two-point).
2. Isometric drawing is the form of pictorial drawing most commonly used in Graphic Communication.
3. Isometric drawing involves 30° angles each side of verticals.
4. Cabinet drawing is a form of oblique drawing in which a front view is first drawn. Lines are then drawn at 45°, along which half scale measurements are taken.
5. Use cabinet drawing with care. This form of drawing can give rise to distortions. When the front view of an object to be drawn is complicated, cabinet drawing may be the best choice.
6. In estimated perspective drawing, vanishing points (VPs) are estimated on an **eye sight** line which is itself estimated at scaled eye level.
7. When using estimated perspective drawing, the position of VPs must be selected so as to avoid the drawing looking distorted.
8. In planometric drawing a plan of the object is first drawn at either 45°/45° or at 60°/30°, from which verticals are drawn.
9. In 45°/45° planometric it is advisable to scale verticals at either 2:3 or 3:4.
10. Orthographic projection can in some cases be used as a pictorial form of drawing.
11. If working freehand there is the same choice. The preferred freehand method is either one-point or two-point perspective.
12. It is when using pictorial methods that colour and shading become important graphic methods.

9 Graphs, Charts and Flow Diagrams

9.1 Introduction

Statistical information such as a series of numbers which have been collected at regular intervals over a period of time, can often be made easier to understand if they are presented in a graphical form — as a graph, chart or other form of diagram. If an **exact** statement of the information is necessary, then a graph or chart should be accompanied by the statistics on which it is based. Graphs and charts show up trends, movements and general relationships between numbers and other items of information. Graphs and charts are not good graphic methods for the presentation of exact information.

Syllabuses for GCSE Technical Communication and Graphic Communication examinations require that candidates can understand and draw line charts, bar charts, pie charts, flow diagrams and operation sequence diagrams. Note that the two terms **graph** and **chart** are used in examination questions as if they mean the same thing. In this book the terms used will be: line graph, bar graph, pie chart, flow chart and critical path chart.

9.2 Line Graphs

Two line graphs, both showing the output of manufacturing industries in Great Britain between 1979 and 1988 are shown in Figs 9.1 and 9.2. Both line graphs take the 1980 figures as 100, with other figures as a percentage of the 1980 figures. Fig. 9.1 shows only the annual rates of production, the plot points so obtained being joined by straight lines. Fig. 9.2 shows the 3-monthly rates with a smooth curve drawn through the points. Both line graphs show the trend — production falling and then rising. The second of the two graphs shows the underlying rises and falls of total production during each year.

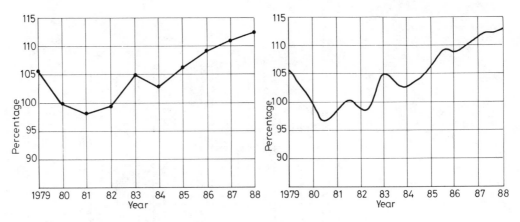

Figure 9.1   A line graph

Figure 9.2   A line graph

Note the following in both line graphs:

1. Line graphs are based upon two **axes** — the horizontal, or x-axis is known as the **abscissa**. The vertical or y-axis is known as the **ordinate**.
2. The x-axis is divided into yearly, or 3-mothly intervals.
3. The y-axis is divided into equal percentage intervals.

9.3   Bar Graphs

The horizontal bar graph of Fig. 9.3 shows the annual profits made by a large company over a period of years. The profits are announced only once a year. This annual accounting makes a bar graph a suitable method of showing the trends given by the figures.

The vertical bar graph of Fig. 9.4 shows the numbers of boys and girls attending a large comprehensive school over a period of 11 years from 1978 to 1988. The graph is really two graphs combined as one. In order to show quite clearly the differences between the numbers of boys and girls each year, the two parts of the graph are shaded. As in Fig. 9.3, the numbers on which the graph is based are taken each year, making the bar graph a suitable method of showing the rises and falls of attendance at the school over a period of years. Note, however, that the graph does not show exact numbers, the y-axis being divided into 100-pupil intervals.

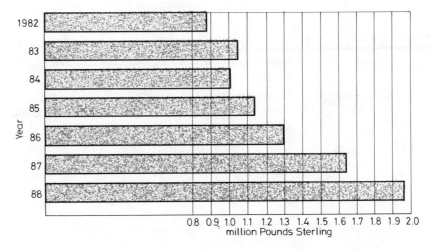

Figure 9.3   A bar graph

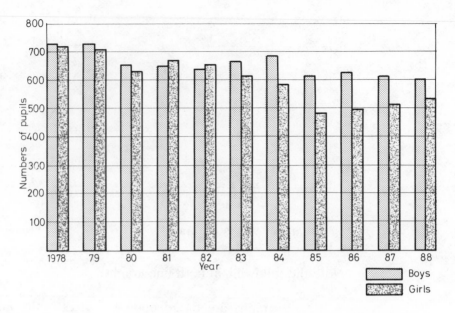

Figure 9.4 A bar graph or histogram

Vertical bar graphs are also known as **histograms**.

Note: Although the two bar graphs of Figs 9.3 and 9.4 have been colour-shaded, this form of graph can be drawn unshaded.

9.4 Pie Charts

The pie chart of Fig. 9.5 is a graph showing the relationship of the numbers in various types of employment of the personnel working in a manufacturing company. The total work force is 320 and these are employed as follows:

   15 are on the management staff.

   50 work in administration.

   10 are sales staff.

   40 are skilled operatives.

180 are unskilled operatives.

   15 work in the transport department.

   10 are cleaners or porters.

To construct the pie chart showing the relationships between the numbers employed in the company in each style of employment, proceed as follows:

1. The number of degrees in a circle is 360. Take the seven figures above in turn and work out the angle of the sector needed to represent the seven types of employment.
2. Draw a circle of a convenient radius.
3. With the aid of a protractor, divide the circle into the seven sectors.
4. Shade or colour the seven sectors.
5. Add a list of the numbers to which the pie chart refers.

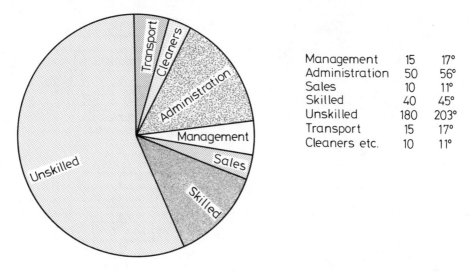

Management	15	17°
Administration	50	56°
Sales	10	11°
Skilled	40	45°
Unskilled	180	203°
Transport	15	17°
Cleaners etc.	10	11°

Figure 9.5 A pie chart

The working out of the angles of each sector is as follows. An electronic calculator was used to work the sums involved:

Management	—	15 —	$\frac{15}{320} \times 360$	=	16.875°
Administration	—	50 —	$\frac{50}{320} \times 360$	=	56.25°
Sales	—	10 —	$\frac{10}{320} \times 360$	=	11.25°
Skilled	—	40 —	$\frac{40}{320} \times 360$	=	45.00°
Unskilled	—	180 —	$\frac{180}{320} \times 360$	=	202.50°
Transport	—	15 —	as above	=	16.875°
Cleaners etc.	—	10 —	as above	=	11.25°
Totals					360.00°

There is no need to work to such fine limits as three decimal places when constructing a pie chart, so the figures used were: 17°, 56°, 11°, 45°, 203°, 17° and 11°.

9.5 Flow Charts

Flow charts are intended to describe the order in which processes should be carried out when performing a task. The Flow Chart of Fig. 9.6 shows the order in which the various processes in making a dress could be performed in order to make the dress satisfactorily. More complicated Flow Charts, such as those shown in the example given on page 139, involve the use of symbols from BS 4058: *Flow Chart Symbols*. Some of the more frequently used symbols from BS 4058 are given in Fig. 9.7.

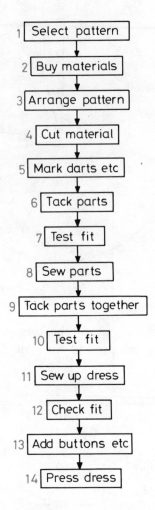

Figure 9.6   A flow chart

Note the following in Fig. 9.6:

1. Each process in the chart is described in as few words as is possible.
2. Each phrase is enclosed in a box frame.
3. Each of the box frames is numbered.
4. The lettering of each phrase is centred within its box frame.
5. Arrows indicating the order in which the processes should take place.
      Note: Arrows need not be added as shown, but some may prefer to include them.

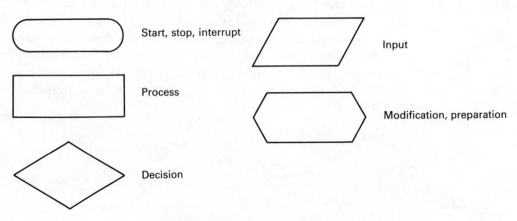

Figure 9.7   Symbols from BS 4058

9.6 Critical Path Charts

If an article is to be made, assembled, finished and packaged for sale from a workshop or factory, a **critical path chart** can be designed and drawn. This type of chart can give information such as the times when to start assembling, when the assembly is ready for finishing and when the finished product is ready for packaging.

Note the following details in the example given (Fig. 9.8):

1. The article to be made consists of three parts — **A, B** and **C**.
2. Part **A** takes 2 hours to machine; Part **B** takes 1 hour to machine; Part **C** takes 4 hours to machine.
3. Parts **A** and **B** must be assembled together before Part **C** can be added to them.
4. Each operation is shown within a circle. Each circle is numbered. The times taken to produce each part are placed above the lines of the chart joining the circles. The figure above each circle is the time taken to produce that part. The figure below the circles is the earliest time the part can be used in the production of the complete article.
5. The **critical path** — the shortest time in which the completed article is ready — is shown by a broken coloured line.

Note: Fig. 9.8 is a simple critical path chart. If many more operations are involved in completing a process, a chart of this type can be much more complicated and give much more information than the simple example given.

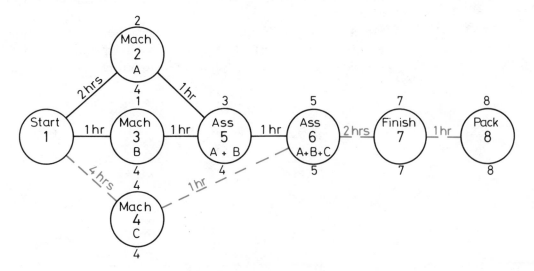

Figure 9.8 A critical path chart

9.7 Worked Examples

Worked Example 9.1

Hilary Gray is sitting her GCSE examinations this year. She is 16 years old.

Her great-grandfather, George Brown (born 1896) married Sarah Green (born 1902) in 1922. Her grandfather, Harry Brown (born 1925) was the second of George and Sarah's five children and he has an elder brother (born 1923) and three younger sisters (born 1928, 1929 and 1931). Nancy Smith (born 1927) married Harry in 1946 and Hilary's mother Joyce, is the eldest of Harry and Nancy's three children, Joyce (born 1947) having two brothers (born 1949 and 1951). In 1968 Joyce married Brian Gray (born 1942) and in 1972 Hilary Gray was born. Hilary has a a younger sister Alison (born 1974).

Construct and draw a diagram showing the relationships between Hilary Gray and her sister Alison and her ancestors down to her great-grandparents. Your diagram should include all birth dates and marriage dates as well as all the given names.

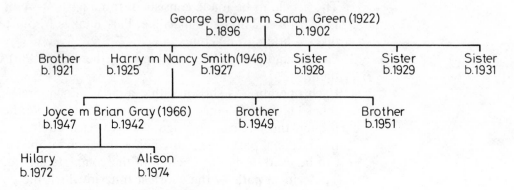

Figure 9.9   Worked Example 9.1

Solution 9.1

Some rough preparatory work on scrap paper was necessary before this solution could be given.

In answering questions of this type, where a fair amount of lettering is necessary it is important to ensure that all printing is as neatly drawn as is possible — either careful freehand or lettering drawn with the aid of a stencil.

Worked Example 9.2

A bar chart showing the range of densities of eight commercial grade metals is given in Fig. 9.10.

Design and draw a different form of chart showing the comparisons between the eight metals.

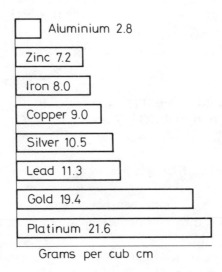

Figure 9.10   Worked Example 9.2

Solution 9.2

Figure 9.11   Solution 9.2

A pie chart was chosen as the different form of chart. No shading or colouring was added in this solution.

To find the various sector angles: Total = 89.8

Aluminium	—	$2.8/89.8 \times 360$	$= 11.22°$
Zinc	—	$7.2/89.8 \times 360$	$= 28.86°$
Iron	—	$8.0/89.8 \times 360$	$= 32.07°$
Copper	—	$9.0/89.8 \times 360$	$= 36.08°$
Silver	—	$10.5/89.8 \times 360$	$= 42.09°$
Lead	—	$11.3/89.8 \times 360$	$= 45.30°$
Gold	—	$19.4/89.8 \times 360$	$= 77.77°$
Platinum	—	$21.6/89.8 \times 360$	$= 86.59°$

The following angles have been used — 11°, 29°, 32°, 36°, 42°, 45°, 78°, 87° giving the required total of 360°.

Worked Example 9.3

A large comprehensive school is organised as follows: The head teacher is assisted by two deputy head teachers and an administrative office staff under a Bursar.

The teaching is divided into six departments or faculties — English and Languages, Humanities, Mathematics, Sciences, Design, Physical Education.

Each department is run by a Head of Department, who is directly responsible to one of the Deputy Head Teachers.

The Bursar is directly responsible to the second Deputy Head who is also responsible for discipline within the school and for parent counselling.

Construct a chart showing the chain of responsibilities within the school.

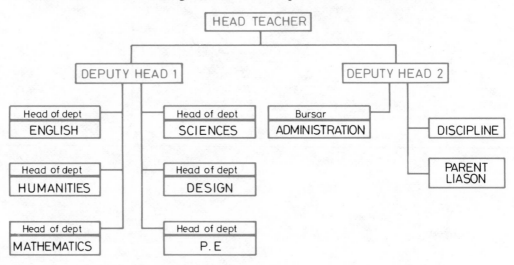

Figure 9.12   Worked Example 9.3

Solution 9.3

This type of diagram is an **organisation** chart. Such charts have to be designed before they can be drawn. This means that the design must be worked out on scrap paper before the drawing can commence.

Worked Example 9.4

A meal consisting of beef casserole, jacket potatoes, carrots and cauliflower, is to be cooked. The cooking times are:

Casserole (beef, onions, mushrooms, stock) — 3.5 hours
Jacket potatoes   — 1 hour
Carrots   — 20 minutes
Cauliflower   — 15 minutes

The meat and vegetables have to be prepared for cooking and the meal must be served hot on hot plates. Design and draw a chart which describes the timing for the cooking of the meal.

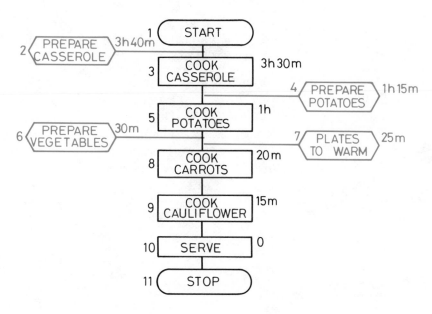

Figure 9.13   Worked Example 9.4

Solution 9.4

Symbols from BS:4058 *Flow Chart Symbols* have been used in the design of this chart in order to show the differences between the cooking processes and the preparation of the item of food making up the meal. In addition the preparation items have been drawn in red.

   Although BS:4058 symbols are designed for use in computer program flow charts, they are quite suitable for inclusion in other forms of chart.

Worked Example 9.5

A District Council requires to show its income and expenditure by means of charts.

(a) Design a bar chart using the information below.

INCOME		(p)
for each £1.00	Taxpayers	36
	Ratepayers	12
	Housing	24
	Service users	18
	Miscellaneous	10
		£1.00

(b) Design a pie chart using the information below.

EXPENDITURE		
for each £1.00	Leisure	(p)
	Environment	15.0
	Housing	17.5
	Planning	45.0
	Transport	7.5
	Administration	5.0

(*LREB*)

INCOME

10p Miscellaneous

Ratepayers 12p

Service users 18p

Housing 24p

Taxpapers 36p

Figure 9.14 Worked Example 9.5(a)

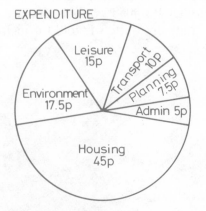

Figure 9.15 Worked Example 9.5(b)

Solution 9.5

Part (a) solution Fig. 9.14 and part (b) Fig. 9.15. Note that no colour or shading has been added to these solutions, because it was not asked for in the question. The working for the pie chart was as follows:

Each p = 360/100 degrees on the chart = 3.6°:

Thus:

Administration	—	5p = 5 × 3.6	= 18°
Planning	—	7.5p = 7.5 × 3.6	= 27°
Transport	—	10p = 10 × 3.6	= 36°
Leisure	—	15p = 15 × 3.6	= 54°
Environment	—	17.5p = 17.5 × 3.6	= 63°
Housing	—	45p = 45 × 3.6	= 162°
Totals		100p	360°

Printing of letters is an important part of the answer to questions of this nature. They can be drawn freehand, or with the aid of a stencil, but must be drawn neatly.

9.8 Exercise

9.1
PART A

About 88% of the salt we eat is already present in food, the remaining 12% is added in cooking or at table:

	%Salt
Cereal products	36
Meat/eggs	24
Cheese/cream/fats	14
Milk	6
Vegetables	6
Fish	2
Added in cooking or at table	12
	100%

Use this information to construct a pie chart.

PART B

Recent changes in wine consumption in nine countries are shown.

Present this information by means of a bar chart. Using this information project consumption of wine in each country in 1987 if present trends continue.

	Litres per head of population	
Country	1969	1978
Italy	115	91
France	112	98
Portugal	98	91
Argentina	88	85
Spain	62	70
Germany	16	24
Austria	8	14
USA	4	7
UK	4	8

(LREB)

Have You Observed the Following Drawing Procedures?

1. It is usually necessary to label the parts of graphs and charts.
2. Lettering is important when drawing graphs and charts. Letters and figures can be added freehand or with the aid of lettering stencils. If freehand, take care to draw neat lettering.
3. The information given by most graphs and charts can be emphasised by the addition of colour or by shading.
4. Show your working when answering examination questions involving arithmetical calculations.
5. Calculations can usually be speedily made with the aid of an electronic calculator.
6. If allowed a choice between bar and pie charts, remember that, while both forms of chart show comparisons between figures in a graphic form, bar charts usually show the information against a scale and so give comparisons based on actual figures. If only the comparison is required, a pie chart is usually the better choice.

10 Engineering Graphics

10.1   Introduction

In Chapter 3 (Orthographic Projection) some details dealing with lines, dimensioning and sections were given. The details given in Chapter 3 apply to other forms of graphics as well as to engineering. In this Chapter further details which specifically apply to engineering graphics are included. Two British Standards Institution publications are of particular importance in engineering drawing. These are:

- BS 308 *Engineering Drawing Practice* — in three parts.
- PD 7308 *Engineering Drawing Practice for Schools and Colleges*.
- PD 7308, which is in one part only, deals with only those details from BS 308 which are in general use in schools and colleges.

Drawings in this chapter conform to BS 308 and PD 7308.

10.2   Lines

Some information about types of lines was given in Chapter 3. Further details relating to engineering drawing are as below.

Six types of line are commonly used in engineering drawings. These can be divided into 2 groups — thick lines and thin lines. Thick lines, whether drawn with pencil or in ink, should be about twice as thick as thin lines (Fig. 10.1).

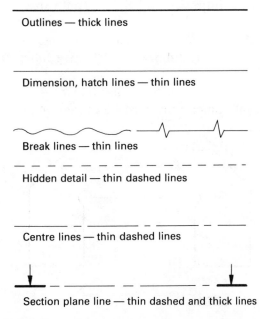

Outlines — thick lines

Dimension, hatch lines — thin lines

Break lines — thin lines

Hidden detail — thin dashed lines

Centre lines — thin dashed lines

Section plane line — thin dashed and thick lines

Figure 10.1   Lines used in engineering drawings

10.3 Lettering and Figures

Capital letters should be used for lettering and notes on engineering drawings, to make sure all lettering can be easily read. In examination work letters about 5 or 6 mm high drawn freehand or with stencils are usually suitable, although some notes may be drawn about 3 mm high. When drawing letters freehand, light guide lines should be drawn to ensure that lettering is of an even height (Fig. 10.2).

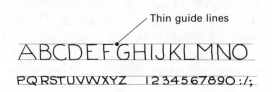

Figure 10.2   Letters and figures used in engineering drawings

10.4 Scales

Scales most likely to be used in examination work are:
Full size and smaller:
   Full size 1:1;   Half size   — 1:2;
   Fifth size — 1:5;   Tenth size — 1:10.

Larger than full size:
   Twice full size — 2:1; Five times full size — 5:1.

Note: All scales are **linear** — all lines are drawn to the scaled length. The full dimensions must be placed on all scaled drawings (Fig. 10.3).

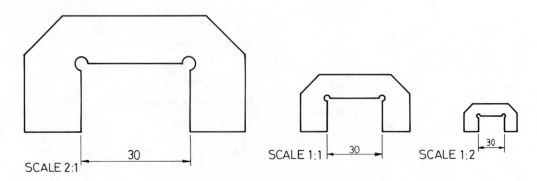

Figure 10.3   Scales

10.5 Screwed Fittings

A number of fittings with screw threads, such as bolts and nuts, are frequently used in engineering. BS 308 drawings of those in most common use are given in Fig. 10.4.

Note: Screw threads are shown in engineering drawings as thin lines.

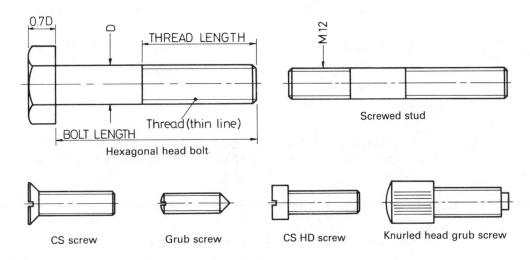

Figure 10.4 Screwed fittings

10.6 BS 308 Conventions

A number of conventional methods of drawing details in engineering drawing are used. Those that GCSE candidates are most likely to come across are shown in Fig. 10.5.

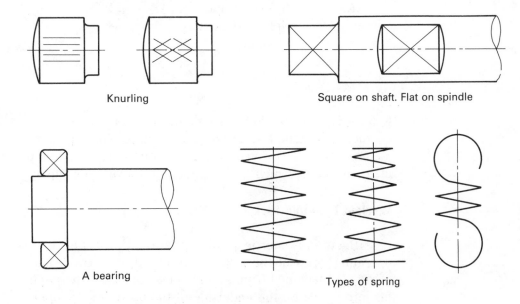

Figure 10.5 BS 308 conventional drawings

10.7 Types of Engineering Drawings

GCSE candidates will see the following types of drawing in examination work:

- *Single part or detail* drawings, in which one part only is drawn;
- *Assembly* drawings in which two or more parts of an article are shown in their assembled state;
- *Parts lists* in which the parts of an article are listed.

These 3 types of engineering drawing are included in the Worked Examples given below.

10.8 Layouts of Engineering Drawings

Most engineering drawings are orthographic projections. Methods of achieving good layouts of orthographic projections are given in Chapter 3 (Section 3.6)

10.9 Dimensioning Engineering Drawings

Sufficient details concerning the dimensioning of engineering drawings for the purposes of GCSE examination work are given in Chapter 3 (Section 3.7). Note the following in addition to the details given in Chapter 3.

Abbreviations placed before dimension figures:

CHAM	— Chamfer
CBORE	— Counterbore.
CH HD	— Cheese head.
CSK	— Countersunk.
M	— ISO metric screw thread diameter.
R	— Radius.
SR	— Sphere radius.
SØ	— Sphere diameter.
Ø	— Diameter.

10.10 Worked Examples

Note: Some of the Worked Examples given below are not taken from purely engineering examples. The given examples should, however, be solved using methods of engineering drawing. In modern examination papers in this subject, many questions which test engineering drawing use this type of example.

Worked Example 10.1

Fig. 10.6 is an isometric drawing of a screw jack. Fig. 10.7 is a front view of the operating screw of the jack. The screw thread, collar and pin of the operating screw are machined from a single piece of steel. The pin of the operating screw fits into a hole on the underside of the head. As the operating screw is rotated the head must not revolve.

Draw, scale 1:1:

A front view and a sectional end view of the assembled screw jack as follows:

(a) Estimate all dimensions not given;

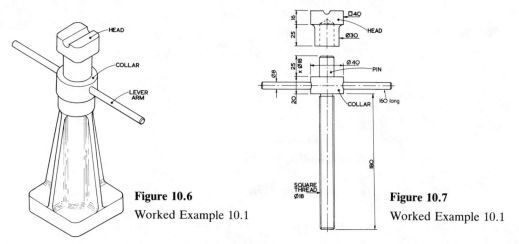

Figure 10.6
Worked Example 10.1

Figure 10.7
Worked Example 10.1

(b) Work in First Angle projection;
(c) The section cutting plane should be taken through the centre of the assembled screw jack.

Add borders to your drawing, a title block and 6 varied dimensions.

Solution 10.1

This Example is a straightforward engineering drawing problem.

Note the following in the solution (Fig. 10.8):

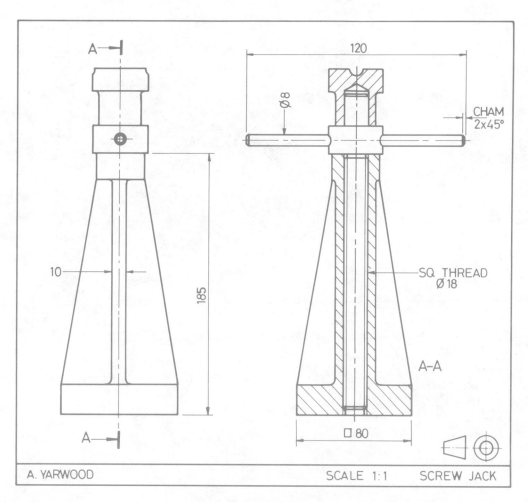

Figure 10.8 Solution 10.1

147

1. Section plane line **A-A**;
2. Sectional view labelled **A-A**;
3. The following are outside views in Section **A-A**:
    (a) The machined operating screw;
    (b) The webs.
But **not** the head — in order to show how it fits on the operating screw.
    4. The 6 dimensions are as varied as possible.

Worked Example 10.2

The photograph (Fig. 10.9) shows a pupil's device for making glass fibre lamp shades. An exploded isometric drawing (Fig. 10.10) shows the way in which the device was made.
Draw within the given borders:

(a) A sectional view as seen in the direction of arrow **S** scale 1:2. The section plane is to be taken centrally through the device;
(b) An exploded isometric drawing of the parts 1, 2 and 3 drawn scale 1:5. The positions of the parts in relation to each other and dimensions not given, should be estimated. Do not draw any hidden detail.

Figure 10.9 Worked Example 10.2

148

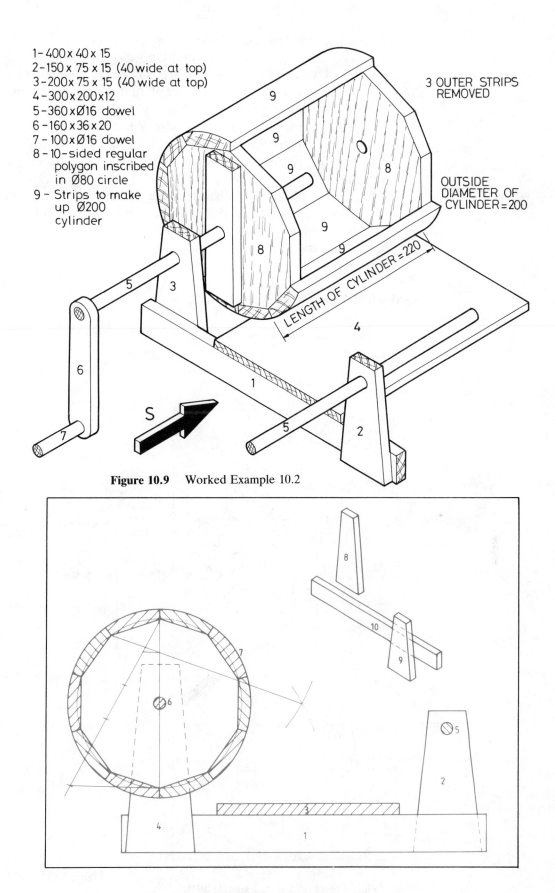

1 – 400 x 40 x 15
2 – 150 x 75 x 15 (40 wide at top)
3 – 200 x 75 x 15 (40 wide at top)
4 – 300 x 200 x 12
5 – 360 x Ø16 dowel
6 – 160 x 36 x 20
7 – 100 x Ø16 dowel
8 – 10-sided regular polygon inscribed in Ø80 circle
9 – Strips to make up Ø200 cylinder

3 OUTER STRIPS REMOVED

OUTSIDE DIAMETER OF CYLINDER = 200

LENGTH OF CYLINDER = 220

S

Figure 10.9   Worked Example 10.2

Figure 10.10   Solution 10.2

Note the following in this solution:
1. The solution has been carefully positioned within the given borders.
2. The DIA 80 circle centred at 6 has been divided into 10 using the method described in Section 2.5, except that the vertical through 6 has been divided into 5 parts. Why only 5 parts?
3. The section hatching of the parts 7 is alternate.
4. In the exploded isometric Part 8 is behind Part 10 and Part 9 is in front of Part 10, but in the sectional view Part 2 is behind Part 1 and Part 4 is in front of Part 1. Why is this?
5. The solution has answered the question without any extras being added — thus titles, dimensioning and the Section letters have not been included. No marks would have been gained by drawing details not asked for in the question.

Worked Example 10.3

An exploded isometric drawing of a Camera Support Clamp is given (Fig. 10.11).

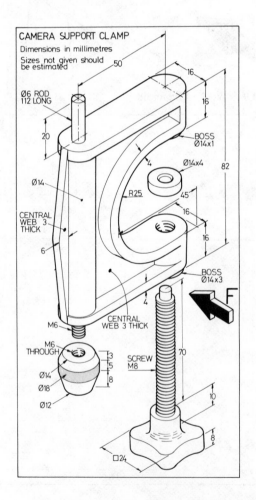

Figure 10.11 Worked Example 10.3

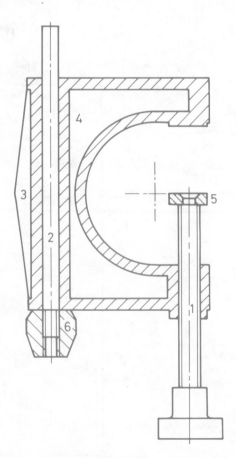

Figure 10.12 Solution 10.3

Draw scale 1:1:

>   A **Front Sectional View** as seen in the direction of arrow **F** with the cutting plane passing centrally through the body of the clamp.

Your drawing should show the parts assembled with the top of the shoe half way across the opening in the body.

Solution 10.3

This example shows how certain features within a sectional view must be shown as outside views. See Section 3.9. Thus the screw (1), the spindle (2), the rib (3) and the web (4) are drawn as outside views within the section. Note also that the shoe (5) and the milled nut (6) have been sectioned in order to show how they fit on to the screw and the spindle.

Centre lines **must** be included.

As in Solution 10.2 above, details not asked for in the question have **not** been added to this solution. No extra marks would have been gained by adding such details.

Worked Example 10.4

The photograph (Fig. 10.13) shows a food mixing machine. An isometric drawing of the stand of the machine is given in Fig. 10.14.

An end view as seen in the direction of arrow **E**, in Third Angle orthographic projection, has already been drawn (Fig. 10.15). In correct projection with the end view, add the following to the given drawing:

(a) A Front view as seen in the direction of arrow **F**;
(b) A plan;
(c) Work to scale 1:2.

Include the constructions used to determine the curves of intersection for the four corners of the vertical part of the stand.

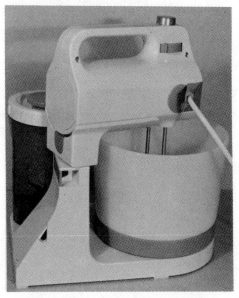

Figure 10.13 Food mixing machine

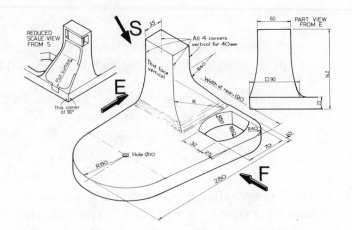

Figure 10.14 Worked Example 10.4

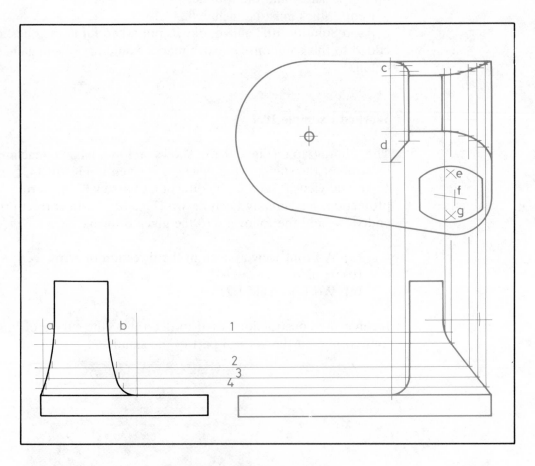

Figure 10.15 Solution 10.4

Both plan and front view 'face' inwards towards the given end view — this is correct Third Angle projection.

The method of construction to obtain the curve of intersection is as follows:

1. Draw the lines 1, 2, 3 and 4 across both front and end views;
2. Where these lines touch the front view, draw verticals to cross the plan;
3. With the aid of a compass, transfer lengths **a** and **b** to **c** and **d** to obtain points on the required curves of intersection;
4. Draw curves through these points.

Note that the centres of arcs in the plan are constructed — **e, f** and **g**.

Worked Example 10.5

The exploded drawing (Fig. 10.16) shows two parts of a clamp used to fasten together two pipes, one vertical and one horizontal.

When assembled around the pipes the clamping is secured by a hexagonal headed bolt (not shown) screwed through the plate.

Draw full size, an orthographic projection, using either first or third angle projection, the following views of the assembled clamp and bolt fastening together the two pipes:

(a) An elevation viewed in the direction of arrow A.
(b) A sectional elevation on the centre line B-B.

The pipes are 150 mm long, 50 mm outside diameter and 40 mm inside diameter. The bolt is M12 × 1.75, 50 mm long and threaded for 40 mm.

The position for the elevation in the direction of Arrow A is given.

(SEG Specimen Question)

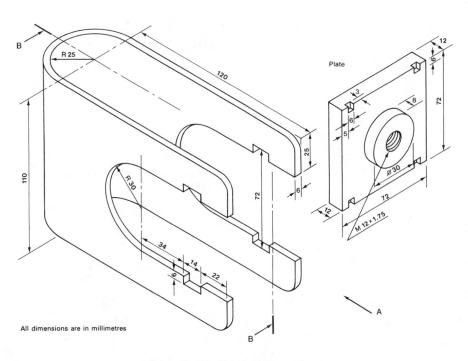

Figure 10.16 Worked Example 10.5

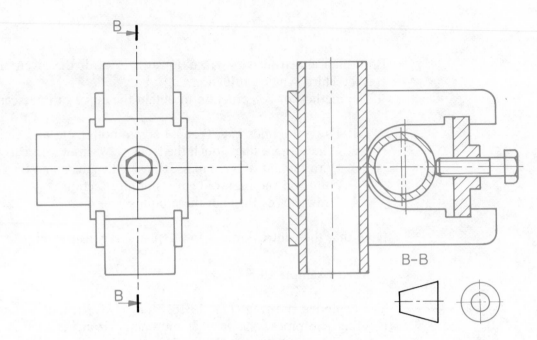

Figure 10.17 Solution 10.5

Solution 10.5

In the given solution (Fig. 10.17) note:

1. Only those details which have been asked for in the question have been included in the answer;
2. Outline lines are thick, centre and hatching lines are thin lines;
3. All centre lines are included;
4. The bolt is drawn in the sectional view as an outside view;
5. Alternate hatching angles;
6. The inclusion of the label **B-B**;
7. BS symbol for First Angle projection completed.

10.11   Exercises

10.1

(a) What do the symbols given in Fig. 10.18 from BS 308/PD7308 represent?

(b) Give the meanings of the abbreviations in Fig. 10.18.

(SREB)

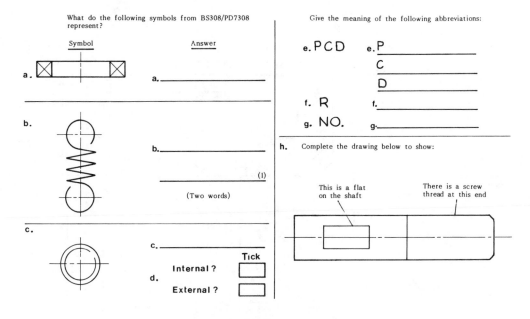

Figure 10.18   Exercise 10.1

10.2

The orthographic drawing (Fig. 10.19) shows three parts of a camera support: 1, the camera mounting bracket, 2 the centre shaft and 3 the bottom plug which is knurled.

On the given centre line make a freehand exploded isometric view of the three parts. The shaft (item 2) has a removable top cap, shown in position in thin chain outline. The only function of the cap is to prevent the bracket coming off the shaft. The mounting bracket should be able to rotate freely as required.

(LEAG)

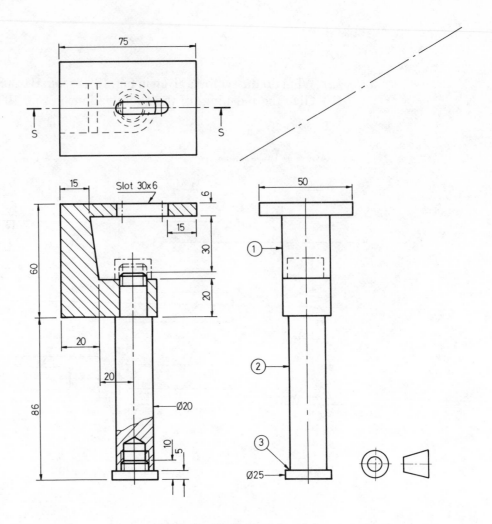

Figure 10.19 Exercise 10.2

10.3

(a) Ten engineering details are listed in the table, Fig. 10.20, and eleven are listed on the drawing in Fig. 10.21.

　　Enter in the table, the numbers which correspond to the listed details.

(b) The end elevation and plan of a casting are shown in Fig. 10.22.

　　Draw, full size, section A-A.

　　Fillet radii may be drawn freehand.

　　Omit all hidden detail.

(Scottish)

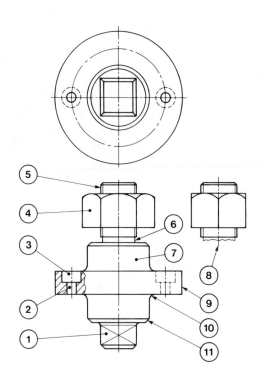

SQUARE ON SHAFT	
FLANGE	
HEXAGONAL NUT	
BOSS	
DRILLED HOLE	
COUNTER BORE	
CHAMFER	
UNDERCUT	
EXTERNAL SCREW THREAD	
FILLET RADIUS	

Figure 10.20 Exercise 10.3

Figure 10.21 Exercise 10.3

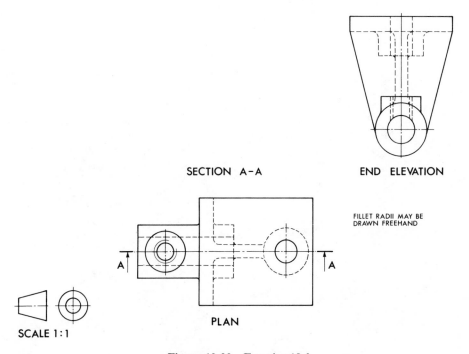

SECTION A-A

END ELEVATION

FILLET RADII MAY BE DRAWN FREEHAND

PLAN

SCALE 1:1

Figure 10.22 Exercise 10.3

157

Have You Observed the Following Drawing Procedures?

1. Check that your engineering drawings are in correct First or Third Angle projection — see Chapter 3.
2. Before commencing an engineering drawing, plan the layout of the views in rough on scrap paper. This will save a great deal of time as a drawing progresses.
3. All outlines should be thick lines.
4. All hidden detail, dimension lines, dimension projection lines, centre lines and section hatching lines should be thin lines.
5. Include all necessary centre lines.
6. Figures for dimensions should be neatly and clearly drawn.
7. Any lettering on engineering drawings must be neatly drawn.
8. Look at the rules for drawing sections in Chapter 3. In particular look at those rules concerning parts which are shown as outside views within a sectional view.
9. Complete title blocks where needed.
10. Include the symbol for First or Third Angle projection.

11 Building Graphics

11.1 Introduction

Two levels of knowledge must be considered for GCSE in Building Graphics. If you choose to undertake a project which includes drawings of buildings, a knowledge of the different types of building drawings is necessary. An example of a project involving building drawing is given in Chapter 14. When answering examination papers, questions are more likely to be set requiring a knowledge of the use of buildings. This chapter is therefore in two parts — the first dealing with building drawings, the second consisting of **Worked Examples** shows the type of questions liable to be set in examination papers.

11.2 Lines in Building Drawings

The same types of lines are used in building drawings as are used in engineering drawings (see Section 10.2 page 143). BS 1192 *Building Drawing Practice* recommends that lines of differing thickness should be used in drawings to ensure they can be easily read. When different thicknesses of line are used, thick lines should be twice as thick as thin lines. The use of different types of lines are shown in the drawings under Section 11.5 below.

11.3 Dimensioning

Dimensions on building drawings follow a similar pattern to those on engineering drawings — see Section 3.7, page 37. Two types of dimensions not used in engineering drawing are shown in Fig. 11.1.

Figure 11.1 Basic and work-size dimensions

11.4   BS 1192 Conventions

Some of the more commonly used conventional methods of showing details in buildings are given in Fig. 11.2.

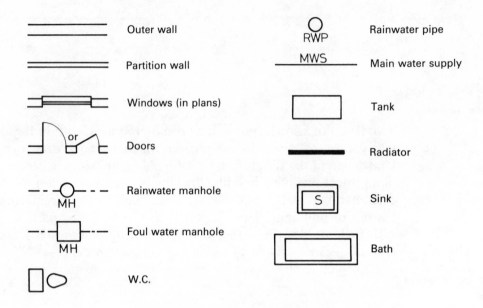

Figure 11.2   Some building drawing conventions

11.5   Types of Building Drawing

Many different types of drawings are used in building graphics. In the designing of any project, such as building a block of flats, building a number of houses on an estate, or building a motorway, a **project set** of drawings will consist of many different types, e.g. block plans; site plans; general location drawings; building drawings; component drawings; assembly drawings. There are other types of building drawings.

In this book, we will only concern ourselves with four types of building drawings:

1. General location drawings — Fig. 11.3;
2. Site plans — Fig. 11.4;
3. Building drawing, or general arrangement drawing — Fig. 11.5;
4. Elevations of buildings — Fig. 11.6.

The building shown in all the four drawings is number 30 Green Lanes.

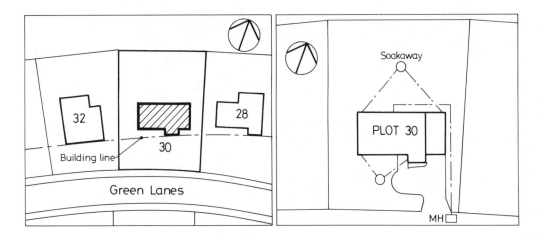

Figure 11.3 General location plan

Figure 11.4 Site plan

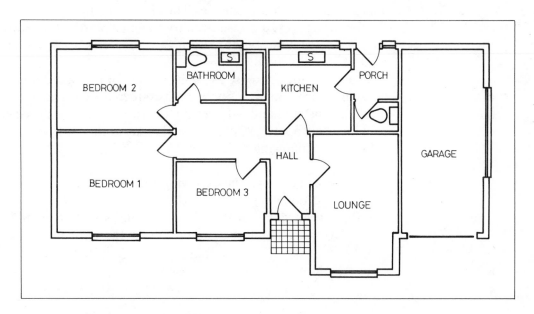

Figure 11.5 Building drawing

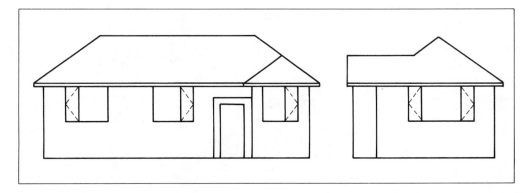

Figure 11.6 Building elevations

11.6 Scales Used in Building Drawings

The following scales are suitable:

Block plans — 1:2000; 1:1000;
Site plans — 1:500; 1:200;
General location drawings — 1:200; 1:100; 1:50;
Component drawings — 1:10; 1:4; 1:1.

11.7 Worked Examples

Worked Example 11.1

The drawing **A** to **L** of Fig. 11.7 shows items of bedroom furniture made as **units**. They have been designed to be stood side by side in bedrooms to give the appearance of fitted furniture. The figures to the right of each unit show the number of items you are allowed to use in answering this exercise. Thus you can have a single wardrobe of pattern **C**, three dressing stools and so on, making a total of 19 units in all.

You are required to use the units to furnish the bedrooms of a three-bedroom house in which a man, his wife and two teenage children (a son and a daughter) live. The husband and wife occupy bedroom 1, the son uses bedroom 2 and the daughter bedroom 3. A plan of the layout of the bedrooms is given in Fig. 11.7

Make the following drawings:

(a) Freehand sketches showing the units placed together for each of the bedrooms.
(b) An elevation scale 1:20 of the units in Bedroom 1. The direction of viewing should be chosen to give the most information.

Sizes not shown are left to your judgement.

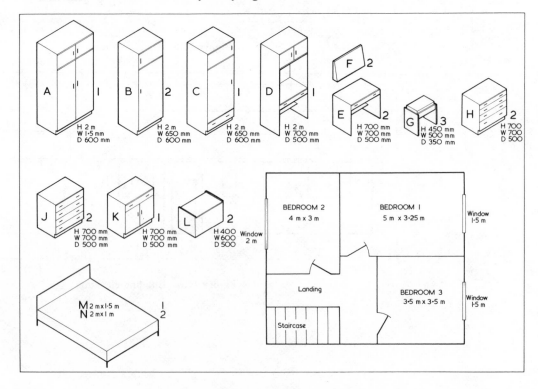

Figure 11.7   Worked Example 11.1

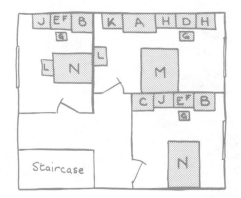
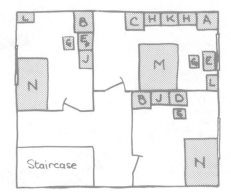

Figure 11.8   Solution 11.1(a)

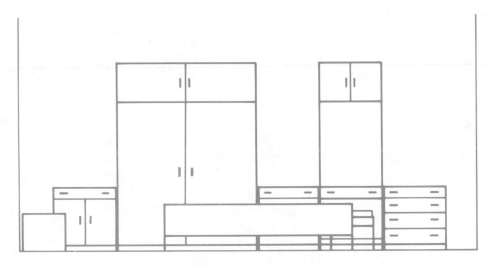

Figure 11.9   Solution 11.1(b)

The solution to part (b) consists of outline line drawings, similar to those given in the question.

Worked Example 11.2

Fig. 11.10 is an isometric sketch of a two-storey detached house. No windows are shown in the sketch. Fig. 11.11 gives the outline of the ground floor of the house, drawn on a square grid showing the positions of the main doors and the staircase.
   Make the two following drawings:

(a) A freehand perspective drawing of the house as seen as if standing on the pavement of the road on which the house is situated and looking at the front and left end. Include the positions of suitably placed windows in your drawing.

(b) With instruments, draw scale 1:50 and using the symbols given in Fig. 11.11 draw a plan of the ground floor of the house to include details of:

   (i) An entrance hall;
  (ii) A dining room;
 (iii) A living room;
 (iv) A kitchen.

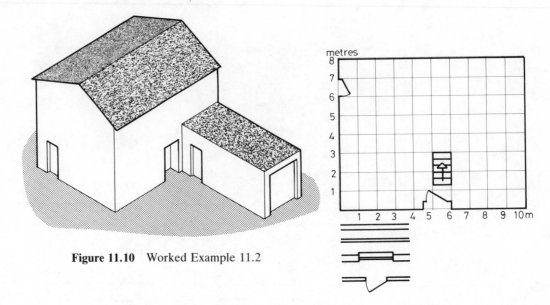

Figure 11.10 Worked Example 11.2

Figure 11.11

Solution 11.2

Figure 11.12 Solution 11.2(a)

Kitchen

Living room

Dining room

Hall

Figure 11.13 Solution 11.2(b)

When answering questions in examinations, there is not enough time available in which to make elaborate drawings. The solution to part (a) is typical — a simple line drawing with no shading and no elaborate details.

Worked Example 11.3

Fig. 11.14 is a plan of a bungalow within its garden boundaries. No paths have been laid and the builder requires drawings to show the positions of all paths needed for the building.

Make the following drawings:

(i) Freehand sketches of the given plan, to include the positions of a coal bunker, washing lines, and a children's play area which includes a slide and a sand pit.

(ii) Using your best sketch ideas as a guide, draw accurately with instruments, scale 1:100, a complete plan of the garden, bungalow and paths.

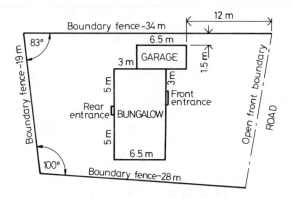

Figure 11.14 Worked Example 11.3

Solution 11.3

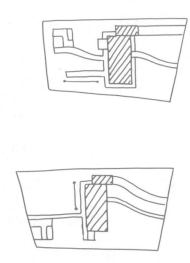

Figure 11.15 Solution 11.3(a)

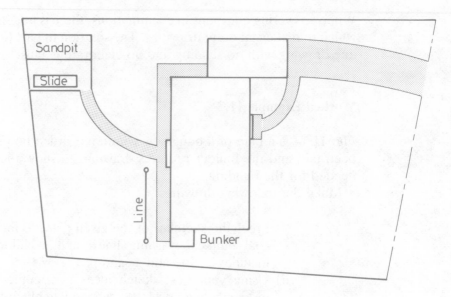

Figure 11.16 Solution 11.3(b)

There are three parts to this solution:

1. The geometrical copying of the given drawing;
2. Freehand sketches to design the required path system;
3. Adding the paths to the plot and bungalow outline.

Worked Example 11.4

Fig. 11.17 is a plan and elevation of part of an empty house, drawn scale 1:20. The kitchen area in divided into 200 mm squares by a grid of lines.

(a) Draw, with instruments, the following items suitably positioned on the plan of the kitchen area:
  (i) A sink with a draining board;
  (ii) A worktop;
  (iii) Storage cupboards;
  (iv) A refrigerator;
  (v) A cooker;
  (vi) The positions of six 13 amp sockets.
(b) Add to the elevation details of the items placed in position against the wall of the kitchen.

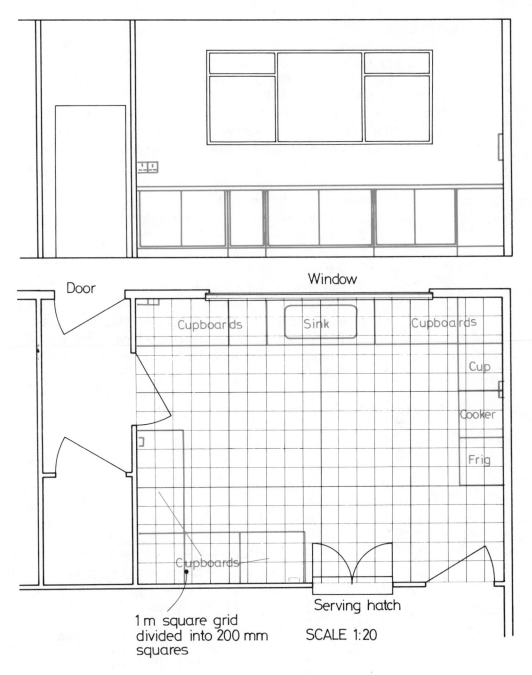

Figure 11.17 Worked Example and Solution 11.4

Solution 11.4

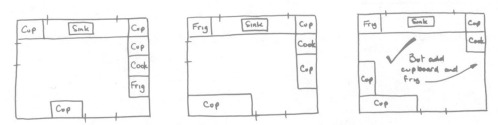

Figure 11.18 Part of Solution 11.4

This solution added to Fig. 11.17 is another in which some freehand design sketches are needed to arrive at a sensible answer.

11.8 Exercises

11.1

Fig. 11.19 gives details of two walls of a fitted kitchen given in a perspective sketch, together with a list of dimensions.

Construct a scale 1:25 PLANOMETRIC drawing of the two walls and the floor of the kitchen showing all fittings in position. Do not include the table in your drawing. Ignore handles, taps and cooker details.

Floor is 3000 mm square.

Ceiling is 2250 mm high.

1. Doors 2000 mm by 760 mm high.
2. Space for washing machine.
3. Cupboard and drawer units — each 1000 mm high by 500 mm wide by 500 mm deep.
4. Sink and draining boards.
5. Cooker — 1000 mm high by 500 mm wide by 500 mm deep.
6. Refrigerator — 1000 mm high by 500 mm wide by 500 mm deep.
7. Wall cupboards — each 600 mm high by 500 mm wide by 300 mm deep.
8. Window — 750 mm high by 1400 mm wide by 75 mm deep.
9. Table.

Note: ALL floor units are 1000 mm high.

(*ULSEB*)

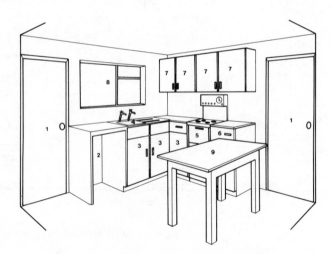

Figure 11.19   Exercise 11.1

11.2

Fig. 11.20 is a two-view orthographic projection of a detached garage, with overall dimensions.

  (a) Draw a freehand isometric sketch of the garage. Colour and/or shading may be added to this drawing.

  (b) Draw with instruments, scale 1:50, a plan of the garage, showing the positions of walls, doors and windows. Suitable symbols for walls, doors and windows are given in Fig. 11.20. Include details of paths.

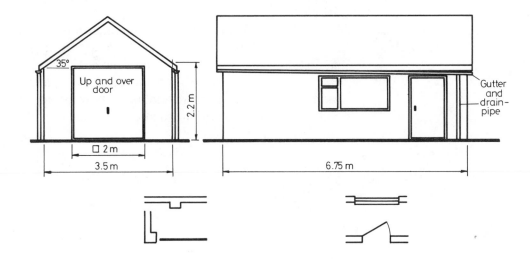

Figure 11.20 Exercise 11.2

11.3

Fig. 11.21 is a sketch of a garden shed. Draw the following:

  (a) A perspective drawing with instruments of the shed as viewed from above. Colour and/or shading may be added to this drawing;

  (b) Scale 1:50 — a two-view First Angle orthographic projection of the shed to include its overall dimensions.

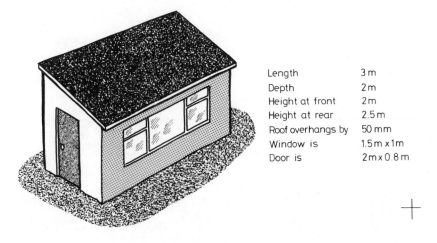

Length	3 m
Depth	2 m
Height at front	2 m
Height at rear	2.5 m
Roof overhangs by	50 mm
Window is	1.5 m x 1 m
Door is	2 m x 0.8 m

Figure 11.21 Exercise 11.3

Have You Observed the Following Drawing Procedures?

1. Lines in building drawings follow a similar pattern as those used in engineering drawings. Make sure you differentiate between thick and thin lines.
2. Scale drawings are important in building drawing. Practice using scales such as 1:20; 1:50; 1:200.
3. Many examples of building drawings will be seen in magazines, in newspapers, in information from estate agents and in brochures giving details about local planning.
4. When revising for an examination look around you at details in your own house, in friends' and relations' houses and in public buildings. Make mental notes of positions of items such as the sizes of fittings, how doors are hung, where doors and windows are placed in buildings, how windows open, layouts in kitchens, how fitted furniture is placed in bedrooms. This sort of information could be of value to you when taking an examination.

12 Design in Graphic Communication

12.1   Graphics is the Basic Tool of Designing

The underlying reason for studying Graphic Communication is so as to be able to use the skills and techniques which are learned, as basic design tools — as the medium by which design ideas can be expressed.

Using the techniques of Graphic Communication, it is possible to discuss design ideas on paper in a graphic form. From this graphic discussion, a design can be developed. Ideas such as: the shape and form of a design; how a design can be constructed; details of the materials which could be suitable for making the design; the appearance of surface finishes; the functions of a design; ergonomics connected with the design. Details about a design such as these are best discussed on paper using graphic methods. When the discussion results in firm design ideas, a solution can be drawn, using graphic methods.

What is particularly important about designing in this graphic form is that ideas can be quickly modified by the amendment of drawings – much more quickly than amendments could be made to an actual design that is being realised (made).

12.2   Graphic Design

All graphics work involves designing. Quite apart from the design of the drawings involved, choices must be made based on knowledge and skills learned in Graphic Communication. Choices such as the following must be made:

Which is the best paper to use;
Whether to work in pen, pencil, colour;
What is the best layout — proportions, balance, composition;
Would colour or shading add to the impact of the work;
How much time is there to complete the drawing;
The cost of the work involved in time and material.

Making choices such as these are essentially design problems, and can only be made on the basis of learned knowledge and skills.

In examinations the design factor in Graphical Communication falls into three main areas:

1. Graphics — choice of medium, layout, etc.;

2. Design questions in examination papers — methods of answering;
3. Project work — this is the main area where design ability can be displayed.

Details concerning (1) are given throughout this book.

Examples of methods of answering examination questions are given below, in this chapter, and also in Chapter 15.

Examples of designing in connection with project work are given in four specimen projects in Chapter 14.

12.3   Graphic Design Methods

Design ideas can be drawn using any of the methods shown in earlier chapters of this book. A summary of the methods available is as follows.

Note that using these methods, drawings can be made either using instruments or working freehand:

1. Orthographic projection in either First or Third Angle, working on plain paper or on square grid paper.
2. Isometric drawing on plain papers or on isometric grid papers.
3. Cabinet drawing working on plain or on square grid papers.
4. Planometric drawing.
5. One-point or two-point perspective drawing.
6. The use of colour to:
    Produce a 3-D appearance.
    To add to the impact of the graphics.
    To draw attention to part of a drawing.

12.4   Finished Drawings

When design ideas have been exploited through the medium of drawings, the time comes when final drawings must be made. Whether the drawing is a piece of graphics in its own right or a drawing intended as a working drawing from which a design is to be made, these final drawings must themselves be designed. Consideration must be given to the following:

1. Which form of graphics is best.
2. The drawing layout must be planned — margins, titles, positions of views, spaces between drawings, type of lettering for notes.
3. Pen or pencil drawings. Instrument or freehand.
4. Colour or shading.
5. Will the drawings require to be mounted. Type of mounting.

12.5   The Design Process

In design work in school and college Craft Design and Technology courses, graphic communication plays an important part as a design tool. The Design Process adopted in many schools and colleges in Craft Design and Technology departments is as follows:

1. *Situation* — State what the situation is that requires a design to solve a problem that has arisen.
2. *Design brief* — Write down the design brief that arises from a study of the situation. A design brief should state clearly what is to be designed.
3. Analyse the problems arising in trying to solve the design brief. Investigate these. Make sketches and notes showing methods of solving these problems.
4. *Ideas for solutions* — Show in sketch and note form, ideas for solutions for solving the design brief. Attempt as many different ideas as possible and do not be worried about suggestions which appear stupid. Some apparently silly suggestions may develop into sound design solutions.
5. During this search for ideas, suggestions for overall dimensions, sizes of parts, materials, constructions, finishes, costs, ergonomic considerations, fittings required, strengths of constructions, safety problems should be noted — again in sketch and note form.
6. From the solutions so far noted choose one as a final solution. Develop this chosen solution until satisfied that a final solution to the design brief has been found.
7. Make working drawings of the chosen solution.
8. Make a model from the working drawing to test the chosen solution — for appearance, to check whether the design will work properly, to test the strength of the design and its parts, etc.
9 Realise (make) the chosen, tested solution.
10. Evaluate the finished design — test it, check it, assess its appearance. Note that evaluation should be part of each stage of the Design Process — e.g. each idea for solutions will need to be evaluated, if a model is made, it should be evaluated. The most important evaluation comes when the design has been completed. This evaluation should be in the form of a written report, which will contain graphics — graphs, charts, drawings suggesting necessary amendments to the design.

Note: Pupils and students at schools and colleges should take note of the fact that the making of modern designs in industry nearly always involves a team of designers. Very rarely will modern design be the work of a designer working on his or her own. Despite this, the practice of designing on an individual basis following a Design Process such as that outlined above is an excellent beginning to understanding how to design.

12.6 Worked Examples

Worked Example 12.1

A garage provides parking, servicing, rescue, tyres and windscreens. It also sells petrol.

In the square provided (Fig. 12.1) draw a suitable sign to show that petrol is sold.

(*LREB*)

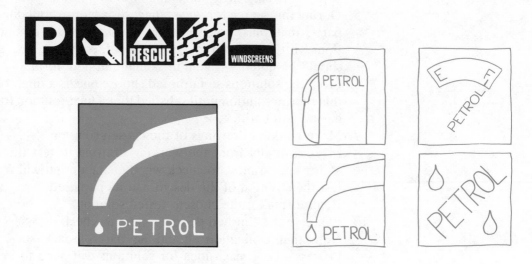

Figure 12.1 Worked Example 12.1

Solution 12.1

Although not asked for in the question, several design sketches have been included in this solution, showing different ideas for the required sign. After consideration of these, one was drawn as the chosen solution.

Worked Example 12.2

The book company Pentangle Publications requires a new logogram. The company specify that the outline of a regular pentagon must be included in the design of the logogram.

(a) Prepare at least three preliminary sketches to explore possible ideas. Take the best features of your ideas and develop a suitable design.
(b) Within the given circle (Fig. 12.2) inscribe the largest regular pentagon. Then, using instruments and incorporating the pentagon, draw your design.

Marks will be awarded for the appropriate use of colour.

(ULSEB)

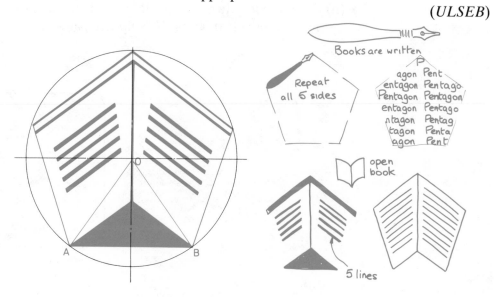

Figure 12.2 Worked Example 12.2

Solution 12.2

Again a solution was chosen from four sketched design ideas and that solution was then drawn with instruments as required. The regular pentagon, inscribed in the given circle, was constructed by dividing 360° by 5 to give 72°, then, with the aid of a protractor, constructing 72° angles from the centre **O** of the circle. Thus angle **AOB** is 72°.

Worked Example 12.3

General information: A new television series is to be produced. It will use
animated puppets and a model satellite to be known as 'Space Orbiter Zero'.
The series will use the name of the satellite as its main title.

A title caption board has to be designed which will introduce each episode.
The producer requires this caption board to consist of a 'space' background with
the letters 'S O Z' appearing centrally on the screen. The letters are to be based
on ellipses (to reflect the elliptical orbit of a satellite) and the arrangement of the
three letters will be the logo which will represent the series.

(a) Design a suitable caption board for this series and draft your design
freehand in the box, Fig. 12.3.
(b) Draft accurately one of the letters which you have designed. Show your
method of constructing the elliptical parts of the letter.

(SEG)

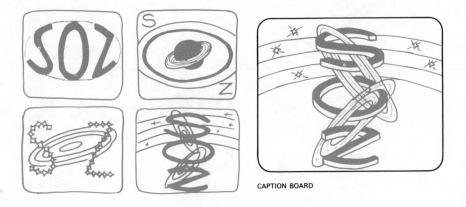

CAPTION BOARD

Figure 12.3 Worked Example 12.3(a)

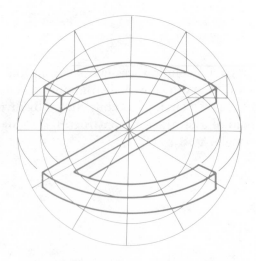

Figure 12.4 Worked Example 12.3(b)

Once again several design ideas have been drawn to meet the given design brief in the question. From the four drawn, one was chosen as a best solution and drawn as asked in the given rectangle.

Note that in the construction of the letter, not all the constructions for the ellipses have been included in Fig. 12.4. This is because so many construction lines were involved in drawing the three ellipses, that the drawing was becoming crowded. However, in an examination all these construction lines should be left on the answer.

Worked Example 12.4

The drawing, Fig. 1 of Fig. 12.5(a) shows the outline of a motor cycle petrol tank. The tank is to be customised by putting the word BIKE on to the side in some form of lettering of 3-D appearance.

(a) In the miniature outlines of Figs 2, 3 and 4 in Fig. 12.5, show **three** possible designs for the lettering.
(b) Draw, to the sizes shown in Fig. 2 of Fig. 12.5(a), an outline of the tank and add your chosen design of the lettering to it. The starting point A is given.

(*LEAG*)

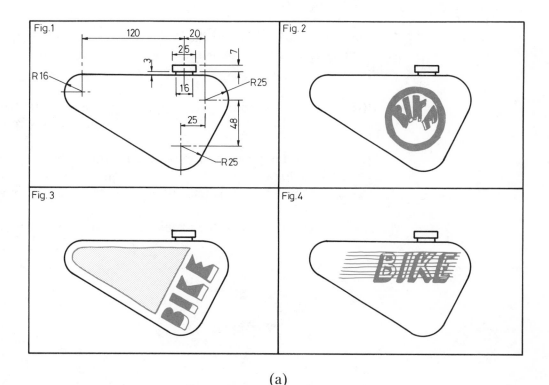

(a)

Figure 12.5   Worked Example 12.4

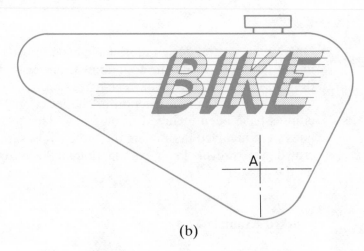

(b)

Figure 12.5 Worked Example 12.4 (*continued*)

Solution 12.4

In the required answer in which the given Fig. 1 has been drawn (Fig. 12.5(b)) to the dimensions given, no construction lines have been included so as to emphasise the most important part of the solution — the design drawing of the world BIKE. However, if answering such a question in an examination, all the construction lines must be included.

Worked Example 12.5

The small holiday island Togoda has a bus service linking the capital Bas with the seaside villages shown on the map. A poster advertising the bus service is now required.

  (i) On the outline of the poster (Fig. 12.6) draw a **simplified** outline of the island and on it draw a diagram showing the bus routes in a **simple** form.
 (ii) In the rectangle in the top right-hand corner of the poster, design and draw a logo which includes the initial letters of the Togoda Bus Company. Design sketches should be drawn in the space indicated.

Marks will be given for the effective use of colour and/or shading.

(*Welsh*)

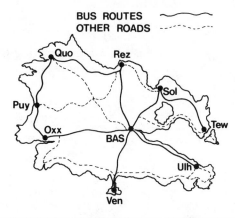

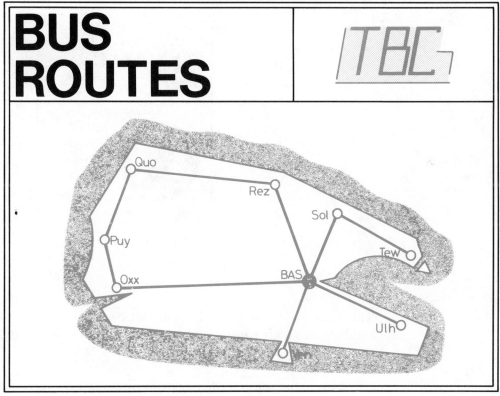

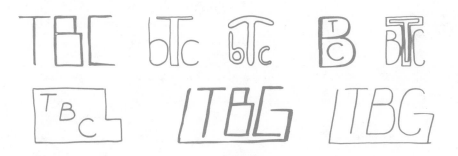

Figure 12.6 Worked Example 12.5

Solution 12.5

In red in Fig. 12.6.

12.7   Exercises

12.1
Two signs giving instructions on safety are given in Fig. 12.7.
In the space to the right of Fig. 12.7:

(i) Draw design sketches for a similar sign to illustrate the statement DO NOT STAND ON SEATS suitable for use on a sightseeing canal boat;
(ii) Draw, using instruments and approximately twice the size of the given signs, your chosen design for a suitable sign.

Marks will be given for the effective use of colour and/or shading.

(Welsh)

Figure 12.7   Exercise 12.1

12.2
The outline of a warning light panel for a car is given in Fig. 12.8. International symbols indicating *Choke in operation* and *Windscreen washer empty* are given in two of the quadrants at the top and bottom respectively.

(i) In the space to the right, draw at least two design sketches for each of the symbols to illustrate:
(a) Sunshine roof open;
(b) Engine overheating.
(ii) Use instruments to draw your chosen designs in the other two quadrants of the panel.

Marks will be given for the effective use of colour and/or shading.

(ULSEB)

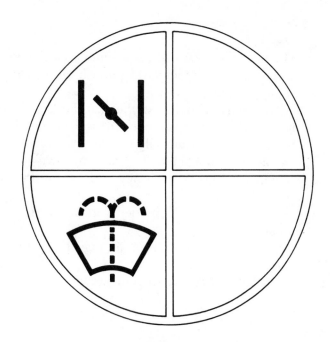

Figure 12.8 Exercise 12.2

12.3

An oil company is to drill a new oil well. A diagrammatic map is required showing the proximity of other wells to the site of the new one.

Given that:

The proposed well is at:	142°30′E, 28°20′S;
There are existing oil wells at:	142°28′E, 27°57′S;
and	142°48′E, 27°36′S;
There is a well drilling at:	141°09′E, 27°51′S;
There is a well with a show of oil at:	143°33′E, 27°27′S;

Complete a diagrammatic map including graduations on the given grid using the given symbols.

An interpretation of a map reference is shown in Fig. 12.9.

(*ULSEB*)

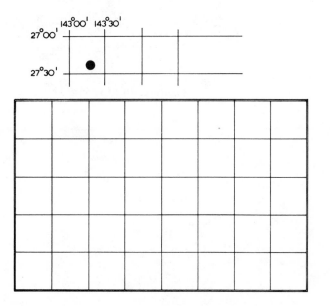

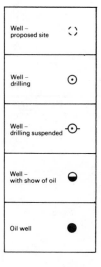

Figure 12.9 Exercise 12.3

181

12.4

The map Fig. 12.10 shows a small area in Gloucestershire.

A local newspaper is to publish an article outlining a scenic cycle ride for young people.

The journey starts at the Car Park at Haresfield Hill. After walking to Haresfield Beacon and back the ride begins. It visits, in order, the viewpoints at Scottsquar Hill, Cud Hill and Painswick Hill, passes a golf course on the B4073 on the way to Painswick, then on down the A46 and along the lane passing Jenkin's Farm. The journey ends at the Public House, south of Edge on the A4173.

Prepare a much simplified version of the map to accompany the newspaper article.

Use the symbols given in Fig. 12.10 to show all important navigational landmarks.

Do not add colour to your drawing.

(ULSEB)

Figure 12.10   Exercise 12.4

Have You Observed the Following Drawing Procedures?

1. When answering examination questions, any design sketches must be included in answers. If they are not included examiners will not know how you arrived at your final answer and marks will be lost as a result.
2. Practise answering design type questions such as are given in Worked Examples and Exercises in this Chapter. Without such practice you may find difficulty in being able to find sufficient design solutions in the limited time available under examination conditions.
3. Graphic designing is of particular importance in the building up of a project folder or folio. Projects in this subject should always include evidence of designing. This could be in the design of the graphics; in showing clearly the manner by which a design functions; and in some examples a Graphic Communication project may be a design study in its own right.
4. The Design process outlined above (Section 12.5) can be followed in a project involving work to a design brief — see the Carrier Bag project in Chapter 14
5. Colour and shading can play an important part in design drawing. However, the suggestion that colour should only be used if its use enhances a drawing apples equally well in design drawing as elsewhere. Do **not** use colour just for its own sake.
6. In projects show as many methods of drawing as possible in design graphics. Moderators will be looking at projects to see if candidates can show variety in their work.

13 Vectors and Circuitry

13.1 Introduction

Questions requiring a knowledge of simple vectors, and of electric, electronic or pneumatics circuits are occasionally set in Graphic Communication examination papers. Although such questions are not set very often, it is advisable to practise drawing vector triangles and simple electric, electronic and pneumatic circuits. You may also wish to include such drawings in project work.

13.2 Vectors

Any quantity which has magnitude without direction is a **scalar**. Quantities having both magnitude and direction are **vectors**. Both scalar and vector quantities can be shown as lines. In Fig. 13.1, line **1** is a scalar quantity — it is a line whose magnitude is 500 mm drawn to a scale of 1:10. Line **2** is a vector — it is a line, scale 1 mm = 1 km/hr, representing a speed of 25 km/hr in the direction of the arrow. Line **3** is also a vector, scale 1 mm = 1 N, representing a force of 50 newtons acting vertically downwards.

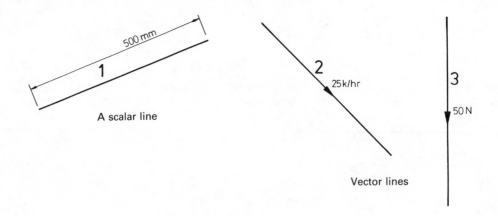

Figure 13.1 Scalar and vector lines

13.3 Worked Examples — Vectors

Worked Example 13.1

Two cars, both starting at point **X** travel along two straight roads as shown in Fig. 13.2. Car **A** travels for 25 km and stops. Car **B** travels for 15 km and stops. How far is car **A** from car **B**?

184

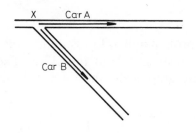

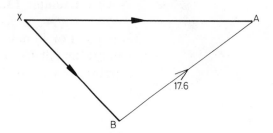

Figure 13.2 Worked Example 13.1   **Figure 13.3** Solution 13.1

Solution 13.1

In the triangle **XAB**, drawn scale 5 mm = 1 km:
XA = 25 km in the direction car **A** travels;
XB = 15 km in the direction car **B** travels;
BA is the scaled distance that **B** is from **A**.
The distance is 17.6 km — measured on line **BA**.

Worked Example 13.2

Fig. 13.4. A ship, **A**, steams steadily East for 50 km from port **P**. A second ship, **B**, steams steadily South for 20 km also from port **A**. How far is ship **A** from **B**?

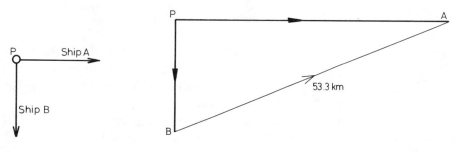

Figure 13.4 Worked Example 13.2   **Figure 13.5** Solution 13.2

Solution 13.2

Fig. 13.5. Triangle **PAB** is the vector triangle of the two ships' movements. Drawn scale 3 mm = 1 km.
  A is by measurement on the triangle 53.3 km from **B**.

Worked Example 13.3

A mass **M** of 40 newtons (approximately 4 kg) is hung from the end of a rod of 1 metre length fixed to a wall, as shown in Fig. 13.6. The end of the rod is supported by a wire. Calculate graphically the forces acting in the rod and the wire.

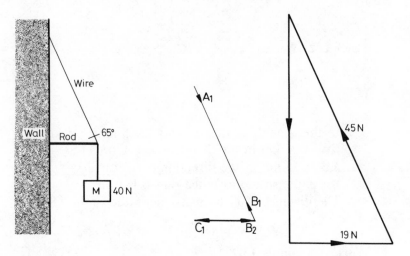

Figure 13.6 Worked Example 13.3   **Figure 13.7** Solution 13.3

Solution 13.3

Fig. 13.7. Note the following:

1. The three forces — the 40 N mass, the force in the wire and the force in the rod — are drawn as a triangle of three vectors, scale 2 mm = 1 N, with sides parallel to the diagram in Fig. 13.6. This vector triangle is a **triangle of forces**.
2. Commence by drawing the vector for the 40 N mass.
3. Then draw the other two sides parallel to the rod and the wire.
4. In this triangle:
   (a) The triangle is closed.
   (b) All three forces act in the same direction around the triangle — clockwise in this case. The arrows on the **vectors** show the directions in which the forces in the system are acting.
   (c) Measuring the lengths of the vectors will give the magnitude of the forces in the system.
5. The forces are found by measuring the sides of the triangle and are:
   In the rod — 19 N
   In the wire — 45 N;
6. By Newton's Third Law, which states that Reaction is always opposite and equal to Action, the force B_1 in the wire AB, must be opposed by an equal force A_1 — if the wire is to remain stationary. Both Force B_1 and A_1 are pulling at the ends A (attached to the rod) and B (attached to the wall). The wire AB must therefore be in tension. In a similar manner, the force B_2 in the rod must be opposed by a force C_1. The Forces B_2 and C_1 are pushing at the ends B (attached to the wire) and C (attached to the wall). The rod BC must therefore be under compression.

Worked Example 13.4

Two forces, **A** and **B**, both acting in the same plane, are pulling at the point **O** as shown in Fig. 13.8. Calculate graphically the single force acting in the same plane, which will hold **O** stationary.

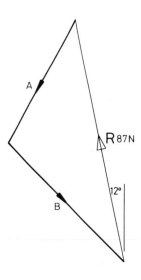

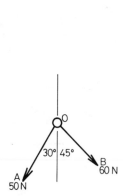

Figure 13.8   Worked Example 13.4   **Figure 13.9**   Worked Example 13.4

Solution 13.4

Fig. 13.9. Note the following:

1. Commence by drawing the vector for force **A**.
2. The two vectors representing forces **A** and **B**, drawn to scale 5 mm = 1 N, are parallel to the two lines of force given in Fig. 13.8. The two vectors **must** be drawn so that the direction of action of their forces is in the **same** direction around the triangle.
3. The line R, which represents the force required in both magnitude and direction. This vector is known as the **resultant** of the vector diagram.
4. The direction of action of the **resultant** in the triangle is the **same** as the direction of forces **A** and **B**.
5. The required force, found by measuring **R** in the triangle is 87 N, acting at an angle of 12° to the vertical.

Note: If the force **R** is now applied at point **O**, the point is said to be **in equilibrium** under the action of the 3 forces. When the triangle of force for a point in equilibrium under the action of 3 forces is drawn, all three forces will act in the **same** direction around the triangle.

13.4 Electric and Electronic Circuits

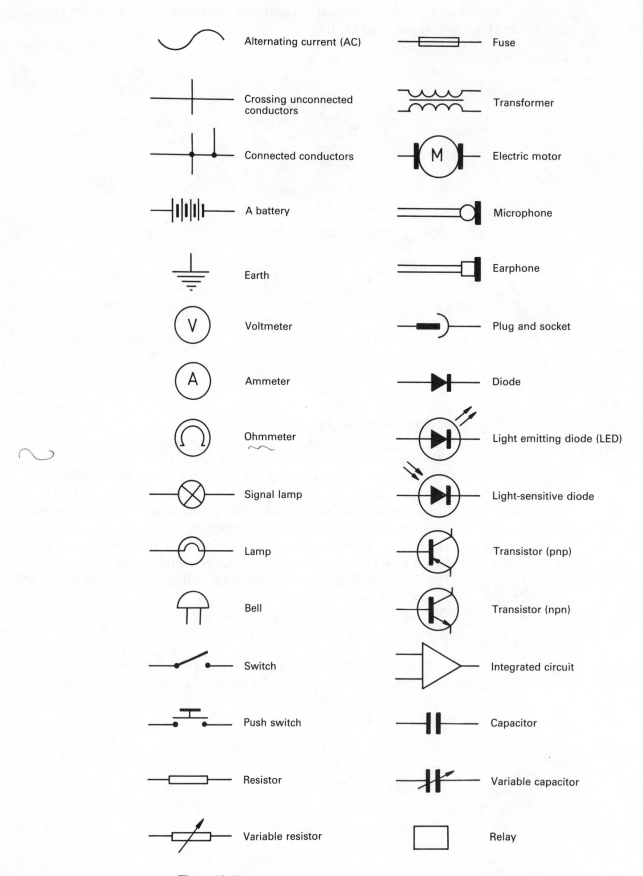

Figure 13.10 A selection of electric and electronic symbols from BS 3939

Fig. 13.10 gives a selection of the more commonly used symbols from BS 3939 *Graphical Symbols for Electrical Power, Telecommunications and Electronic Diagrams*. It would be quite impossible to show all the symbols from this very large British Standard here in this book. Those which the GCSE candidate are most likely to come across are included.

13.5   Worked Examples — Electric and Electronic Circuits

Worked Example 13.5

A push switch is connected via a fuse and a single lamp to an electric motor. In parallel with the motor is a lamp with its own switch. The circuit is connected to an earthed 240 V alternating current supply. The signal lamp indicates that the motor is switched ON or OFF; the other lamp provides light for a person using the motor.

Draw, with instruments and using the symbols given in Fig. 13.11, the circuit diagram described.

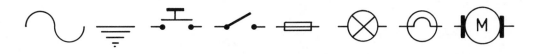

Figure 13.11   Worked Example 13.5

Solution 13.5

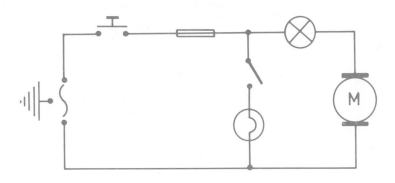

Figure 13.12   Solution 13.5

Worked Example 13.6

A sketch of a circuit for an experiment in a course in electric circuitry in a school is shown in Fig. 13.12.

Selecting symbols from those given with Fig. 13.12 draw, with instruments, a diagram for the circuit.

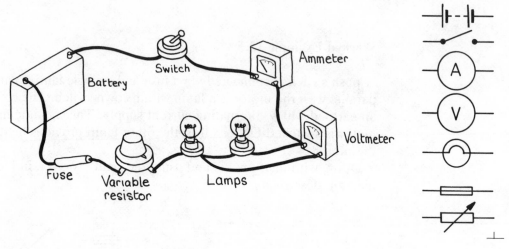

Figure 13.13   Worked Example 13.6

Solution 13.6

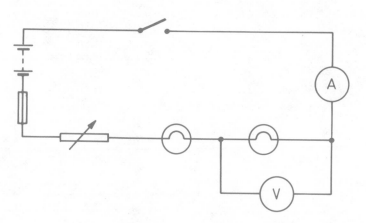

Figure 13.14   Solution 13.6

Worked Example 13.7

A sketch of a light-operated switching circuit, mounted on a board, is shown in Fig. 13.15. Selecting symbols from those given, draw with instruments, a circuit diagram of the light-operated switch.

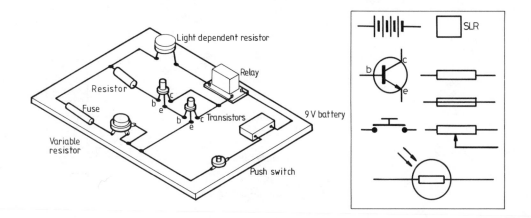

Figure 13.15   Worked Example 13.7

Solution 13.7

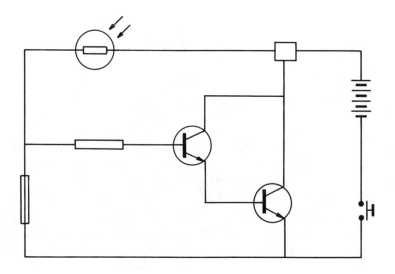

Figure 13.16   Solution 13.7

13.6 Pneumatics Circuits

It is unlikely that questions will be set in examination papers asking for the drawing of pneumatics circuits. However, if you are interested, drawings of pneumatic circuits may be of value in project work. A short section on this topic is therefore included here.

13.7   Symbols for Pneumatic Components

The British Standard BS 2917 deals with the graphics for pneumatics circuits. Some of the more common symbols from that Standard are given in Fig. 13.17.

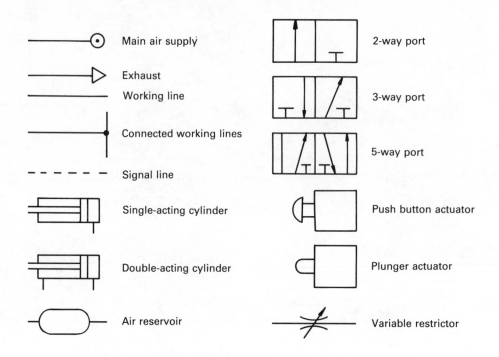

Figure 13.17   A selection of pneumatics circuit symbols from BS 2917

13.8   Examples of Pneumatic Circuits

Three drawings — Figs 13.18, 13.19 and 13.20, show pneumatics circuits.

Fig. 13.18 — a simple circuit showing a single-acting cylinder controlled by a 3-port valve with a plunger actuator. This drawing shows the circuit in its **un-operated** state — before the plunger has been pressed. This is how pneumatics circuits should **always** be drawn.

Fig. 13.19 shows the same circuit in its **operated** state — after the plunger has been pressed. Pneumatic circuits should **not** be drawn in the **operated** state, which is why the drawing is shown crossed out.

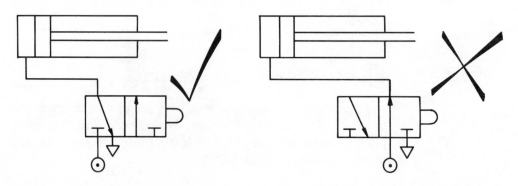

Figure 13.18   Pneumatic circuits — control of single-acting cylinder

Figure 13.19   Wrongly drawn pneumatics circuit

Fig. 13.20 is a more complicated pneumatics circuit of a speed control circuit using the following components:

A double-acting cylinder.

Two 3-port valves, one actuated by a plunger, the second actuated by a roller lever.

A 5-port valve.

A reservoir.

An exhaust restrictor.

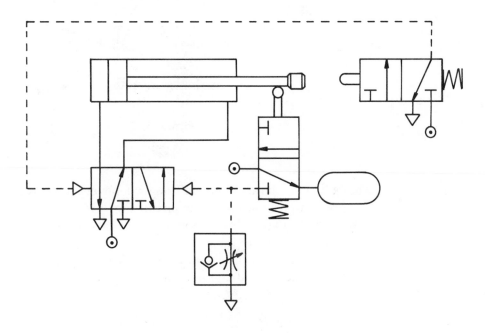

Figure 13.20 Pneumatics circuits — speed control

13.9 Exercises

13.1

Front and end views of a shelf of books are given in Fig. 13.21. Calculate by drawing a triangle of forces, the forces in the bars AB and BC of each of the shelf supports. Which of the bars is in compression and which in tension? Assume that the force exerted downwards by the articles on the shelf is shared equally between the two shelf supports.

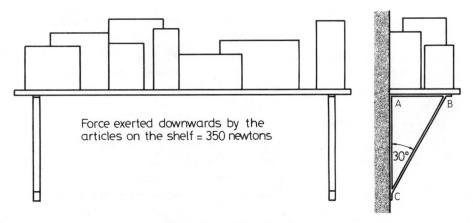

Force exerted downwards by the articles on the shelf = 350 newtons

Figure 13.21 Exercise 13.1

13.2

Two people can just move a load of bricks on a trolley by applying force as shown in Fig. 13.22. Calculate, by drawing a triangle of forces, the force and its direction which would have to be applied by one person to just move the trolley.

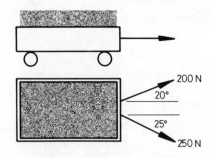

Figure 13.22   Exercise 13.2

13.3

The bell of an alarm system will ring whenever a door is opened by releasing the compressed push switch in the circuit Fig. 13.23.

By inserting another component in the layout this will allow the system to be set to operate when and as required.

Using the symbols as given, draw a circuit diagram of this sytem which should include the additional component.

(SREB)

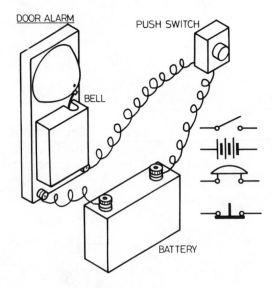

Figure 13.23   Exercise 13.3

13.4

(a) A man has a battery, a bulb and one length of wire which he can bend but not cut. Show by means of a circuit diagram how he gets the bulb to light. Use drawing instruments.

(b) The surface colouring of aluminium can be achieved by thickening the natural oxide film already present in the material. This process is called anodising.

The drawings, Fig. 13.24, show:
    A A plastic container.
    B The prepared workpiece to be anodised (anode).
    C Two lead plates (cathode).
    D The electrolyte (acid bath).
   Show by means of a circuit diagram how the workpiece is anodised. Use drawing instruments.

(LREB)

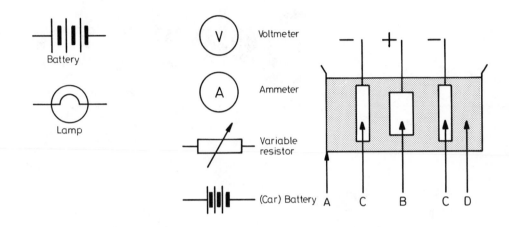

Figure 13.24 Exercise 13.4

Have You Observed the Following Drawing Procedures?

1. A **scalar** quantity has magnitude only, a **vector** quantity has direction as well as magnitude.
2. If a triangle of forces represents a point in **equilibrium** then the forces should act in the same direction around the triangle.
3. When drawing electric or electronic circuits, the circuit must be complete — all components should be joined to each other by conductor lines. If there is a break in the circuit, it will not work.
4. Pneumatics circuits must be drawn in their **unoperated** state.

14 Graphic Communication Projects for GCSE

14.1　Project Requirements

All the GCSE boards require project work (sometimes known as course work) from candidates taking Graphic Communication and Technical Communication examinations. Each of the boards has slightly different requirements when moderating and marking project (or course) work. However, they all have many in common, as follows:

1. The project will carry **30%** of the total marks for the examination, except in the case of the Midland Examining Board, when the project carries **40%** of total marks.
2. The boards may require either:
   (a) that the project title be chosen from a list published by the board, **or**;
   (b) the project title is chosen by the teacher or lecturer, **or**;
   (c) the project title is chosen by the candidate.
3. The moderators appointed by the boards, who will be marking the projects are looking to see if candidates can present to them sheets of **good quality graphical work** showing a **variety** of graphic techniques.
4. The sheets of graphics should be contained either in a well-designed **folder** or in a **folio**, or should be mounted separately on boards or other backing material. Presentation is very important. It is up to you to impress the moderator. Well-presented sheets of drawings will get you off to a good start.
5. Models, photographs, films, video tapes, computer printouts and other material such as these, which may back-up your graphics, can be included in a project.
6. The general requirement is that project work should occupy about between **30** and **40** hours of work during at least the last two terms prior to the examination date.
7. Some boards stipulate that at least 10 sheets of drawings are needed. All the boards suggest that A2 or A3 sheets are good sizes on which to present project work. If smaller sheets are included, it is suggested that they be mounted on A2 or A3 sheets.

8. The work **must** be your own. Moderators are usually instructed to look for signed statements to the effect that the work being submitted is the candidate's own. Help given to the candidate should be supported by a written statement giving details of the assistance that has been given.

9. The work included in your project need not necessarily be wholly original, although evidence of research, any preliminary work and some designing is expected. If your preliminary planning is in rough note and sketch form it must be included with the other work in your project. Do not forget that these rough notes and sketches should be well and properly mounted within your whole project.

14.2   What to Include in a Project Folio

The following can be included in your project:
Orthographic projections.
Isometric drawings.
Exploded isometric drawings.
Cabinet drawings.
Exploded cabinet drawings.
Freehand drawings — orthographic, isometric, cabinet, perspective.
Notes on research, planning and preliminary work.
Draft sketches in pen or pencil.
Notes of modifications.
Diagrams, graphs, charts (bar, flow, critical path).
Colour pen or pencil work.
Colour wash work.
The use of dry transfers.
Computer printout.
Photographs of computer screen results.
Other photographs.
Models.
Videotapes.
Audio tapes — if appropriate.
Drawings on grid papers.
Circuit diagrams.
Developments.

14.3   Specimen Projects

The following specimen projects are shown here as being typical of the type of work which examination moderators will be looking for when they are marking your project. Each of the four projects shown here is based upon work which has been submitted by candidates in Technical Communication and Graphic Communication examinations. The four specimen projects are:

1. *An Analysis of a Manufactured Product* — This project is of the type which requires a good knowledge of engineering drawing. Details of the parts of the product, the manner in which they are assembled, and an analysis of the movements of a lamp mechanism are given in several sheets of drawings.

2. *A Computer Programming Project* — All the programs in this project have been designed to produce graphics on a computer screen when the programs are RUN
3. *A Graphic Design Project* — This project involved the designing of an article in everyday use.
4. *A Building Drawing Project* — This involved a variety of building drawing techniques as well as other forms of graphics.

Note: Not all of the sheets of drawings from the specimen projects have been included here because of lack of space in a book of this nature. However, sufficient sheets of graphics have been included in the following pages to show quite clearly how a graphic project should be developed and presented.

The following graphic techniques and methods have been included in the pages which show the four projects:

Engineering drawing.
First and Third Angle orthographic projection.
Exploded orthographic projections.
Isometric drawing.
Cabinet drawing.
Freehand drawing.
The use of dry transfers.
The inclusion of photographs in a project.
The design of folio covers.
Colouring with pen and pencil.
Colouring with water colour.
Freehand printing.
Computer printouts.
Computer programming in BASIC.
Photographs of computer screens.
Rough notes and sketches.

Note: No matter how rough your preparatory notes and sketches may be, they should be included in a project folio. It must be remembered that moderators must look for **good quality graphics** and rough work on its own is completely useless if you are seeking good marks. If however, your rough work is not submitted, it is very difficult for moderators to determine how you have arrived at the work you are submitting.

14.4 An Analysis of a Manufactured Product

Project — A Lamp Mechanism

This project consists of 12 sheets of drawings in a folder, the cover of which has been designed for the purpose. Only the folder cover and the first eight sheets of the 12 are included here. The sheets of graphics have been numbered in sequence with Letraset figures in the bottom right-hand corner of each sheet. A variety of graphic techniques have been employed in compiling this project as follows:

First and Third Angle orthographic projection.
Isometric drawing.
Cabinet drawing.
Freehand drawing.
The use of Letraset dry transfer lettering.
The use of lettering stencils.
The use of an ellipse template.

The inclusion of photographs in a graphic project.

Tinting with water colour.

Two-colour work in pen and pencil.

An analysis of a linkage movement.

The design of a folder cover.

The complete set of 12 drawings is:

Cover — Fig. 14.1 — a photograph of the lamp mechanism mounted on card and enclosed within a line frame, with Letraset dry transfer lettering naming the project and the candidate.

Sheet 1 — Fig. 14.2 — a 3-dimensional view of the assembled mechanism in First Angle projection. Numbers in balloons indicate the parts of the mechanism which are referred to in later drawings.

Sheet 2 — Fig. 14.3 — a front view of the mechanism showing the extent of the reach of the arms.

Sheet 3 — Fig. 14.4 — a 3-dimensional drawing with details of possible movements of the mechanism for positioning the lamp — up; down; backwards; forwards; any position in a circle based on the position of Part 8 — horizontally through 270 degrees, together with a possible 180 degrees movement based on the mechanism of Part 3.

Sheet 4 — Fig. 14.5 — Third Angle projections — details of Part 2. All the pieces of Part 2 have been drawn as if **exploded** in line with the pieces to which each is attached. Drawings partly dimensioned with main sizes.

Sheet 5 — Fig. 14.6 — Third Angle projection of Part 3 together with a cabinet drawing of pieces making up Part 3. Details of Part 6 are also included on this sheet.

Sheet 6 — Fig. 14.7 — orthographic and isometric drawings of the bars of the mechanism, including details of the nuts, bolts, spindles and sleeves which join the bars to each other.

Sheet 7 — Fig. 14.8 — First Angle projection of Part 8 together with an isometric drawing of the part. Also included are details of the springs which allow the mechanism to remain in position wherever it may be placed.

Sheet 8 — Fig. 14.9 — freehand, tinted drawings of three different types of mounting into which the mechanism can be fitted.

Not included here:

Sheet 9 — Freehand drawings of a variety of lamp shades which could be fitted in place of that shown in *Sheet 1*.

Sheet 10 — Photographs of three other types of lamp mechanisms which allow positioning of light from a lamp.

Sheet 11 — A drawing of a design for a mounting which would allow the mechanism to be fitted to a sloping desk top.

Sheet 12 — An Index of sheets.

(a) Model

In addition to the 12 sheets of graphics in their folio a model of the mechanism was included in the project submitted for examination marking. This was made from strips of 10 mm square wood with pins and nuts and bolts for pivots. The model was made full size, its purpose being to show all possible movements of the linking bars.

Figure 14.1 Project folio cover for lamp mechanism

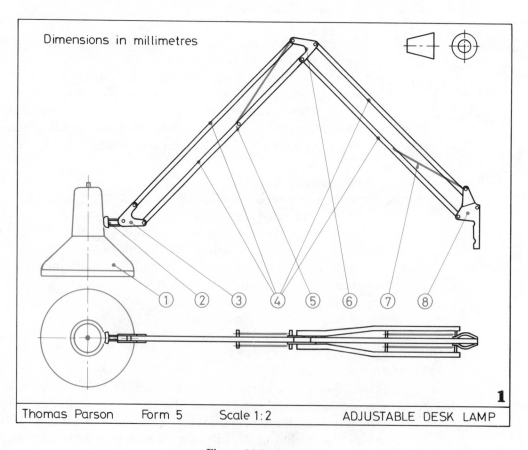

Dimensions in millimetres

① ② ③ ④ ⑤ ⑥ ⑦ ⑧

Thomas Parson   Form 5   Scale 1:2   ADJUSTABLE DESK LAMP

1

Figure 14.2 Sheet 1

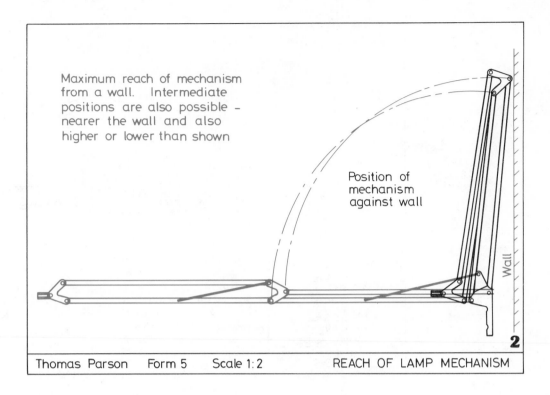

Figure 14.3 Sheet 2

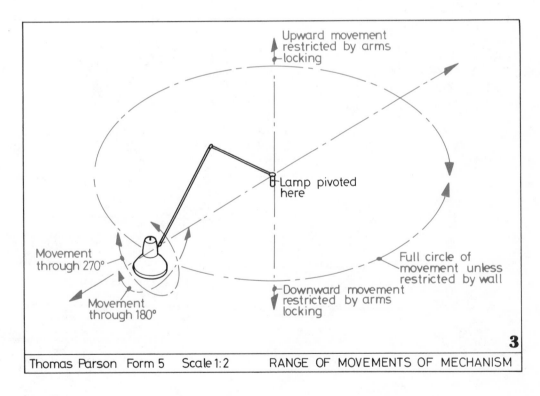

Figure 14.4 Sheet 3

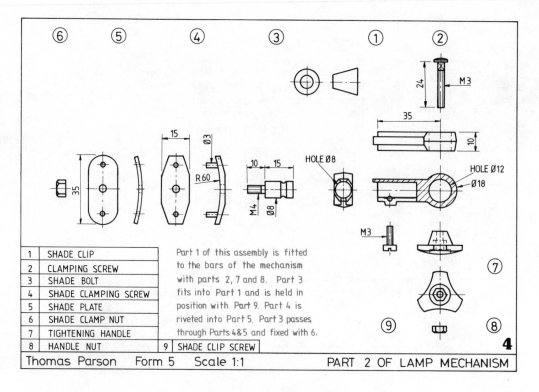

1	SHADE CLIP
2	CLAMPING SCREW
3	SHADE BOLT
4	SHADE CLAMPING SCREW
5	SHADE PLATE
6	SHADE CLAMP NUT
7	TIGHTENING HANDLE
8	HANDLE NUT
9	SHADE CLIP SCREW

Part 1 of this assembly is fitted to the bars of the mechanism with parts 2, 7 and 8. Part 3 fits into Part 1 and is held in position with Part 9. Part 4 is riveted into Part 5. Part 3 passes through Parts 4 & 5 and fixed with 6.

4

Thomas Parson   Form 5   Scale 1:1   PART 2 OF LAMP MECHANISM

Figure 14.5   Sheet 4

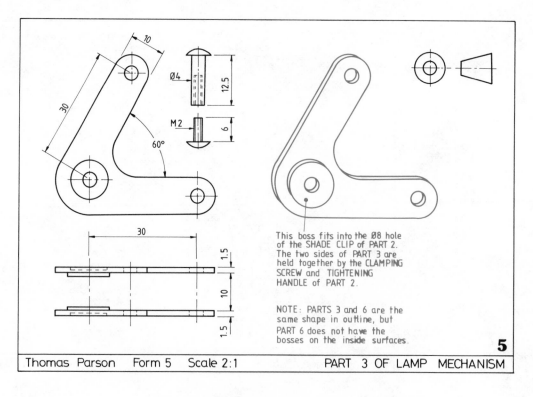

This boss fits into the Ø8 hole of the SHADE CLIP of PART 2. The two sides of PART 3 are held together by the CLAMPING SCREW and TIGHTENING HANDLE of PART 2.

NOTE: PARTS 3 and 6 are the same shape in outline, but PART 6 does not have the bosses on the inside surfaces.

5

Thomas Parson   Form 5   Scale 2:1   PART 3 OF LAMP MECHANISM

Figure 14.6   Sheet 5

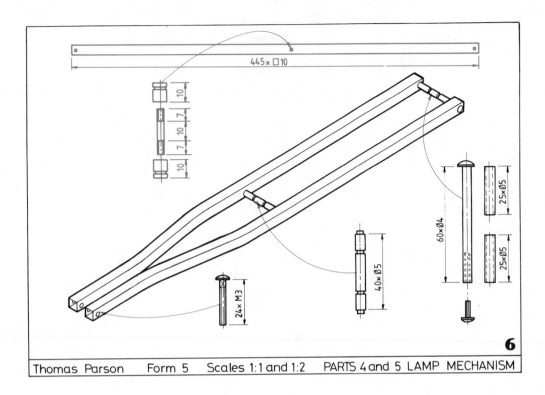

6

Figure 14.7   Sheet 6

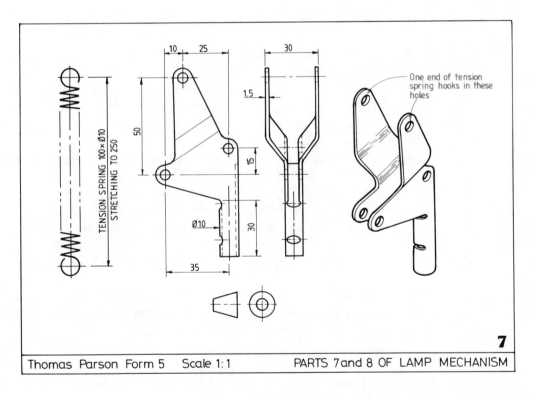

7

Figure 14.8   Sheet 7

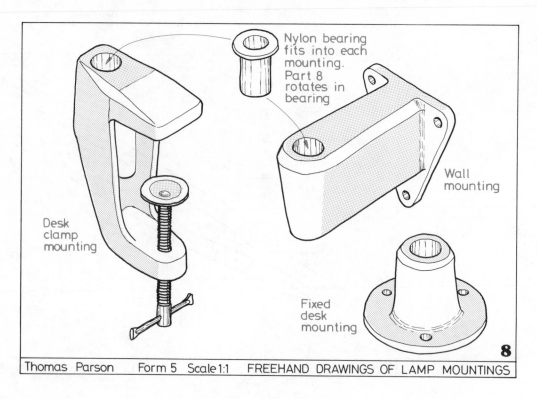

Nylon bearing fits into each mounting. Part 8 rotates in bearing

Wall mounting

Desk clamp mounting

Fixed desk mounting

8

| Thomas Parson | Form 5 | Scale 1:1 | FREEHAND DRAWINGS OF LAMP MOUNTINGS |

Figure 14.9 Sheet 8

14.5 A Computer Program Project

This project is the result of 20 programs written in BBC BASIC on a BBC B computer. The programs were designed to show the various graphics possibilities which can be produced when programming for BBC computers. Each program is preceded with short notes which appear on the screen to explain how to RUN the programs and what will appear on the computer screen when the programs are run.

The complete project consisted of 16 sheets of graphics and notes, together with a 133 mm (5.25 inch) floppy disk on which the programs had been SAVED. Only four of the programs are included here because of lack of space. However, these four do show the methods of programming which were employed in this project. The code names of the programs which have been included here are:

PRCOVER (Fig. 14.10); PAGE2 (Fig. 14.11);
DOGS (Fig. 14.12); PATTERN (Fig. 14.13)

The project folder included printouts of the computer programs and of the graphics produced by them. Also included were some diagrams, a few flow charts, some sheets of notes (in printout form), some photographs and the floppy disk.

The complete project consisted of:

Sheets A to D — Figs 14.14 to 14.17 — notes typed on a computer with the aid of a word processor chip and a printer.

Sheets 1 to 4 — Figs 14.18 to 14.21 — on which Figs 1 to 9, referred to in the notes, are given.

5 sheets of computer printouts showing all 20 programs.

2 sheets of computer printouts of the graphics produced by the programs — Figs 14.22 to 14.25 show four of these.

2 sheets of photographs of the results of the programs on a computer screen — Figs 14.26 to 14.31 show six of these.

204

PROGRAM — PRCOVER

```
10 REM ***PROJECT COVER ***
20 MODE 7
27 81 60
30 PRINTTAB(0,2)CHR$130"************************************"
40 PRINTTAB(13,3)CHR$141CHR$131"MY COMPUTER"
50 PRINTTAB(13,4)CHR$141CHR$131"MY COMPUTER"
60 PRINTTAB(15,5)CHR$141CHR$131"PROGRAM"
70 PRINTTAB(15,6)CHR$141CHR$131"PROGRAM"
80 PRINTTAB(15,7)CHR$141CHR$131"PROJECT"
90 PRINTTAB(15,8)CHR$141CHR$131"PROJECT"
100 PRINTTAB(0,9)CHR$130"************************************"
110 PRINTTAB(6,14)CHR$141CHR$133"CONSTRUCTIONAL   GEOMETRY"
120 PRINTTAB(6,15)CHR$141CHR$133"CONSTRUCTIONAL   GEOMETRY"
130 PRINTTAB(0,12)CHR$146CHR$157
140 PRINTTAB(38,13);CHR$146CHR$255
150 PRINTTAB(0,13);CHR$146CHR$255
160 PRINTTAB(38,17)CHR$146CHR$255
170 PRINTTAB(0,17)CHR$146CHR$255
180 PRINTTAB(0,18)CHR$146;CHR$157
190 PRINTTAB(0,21)CHR$134"RANJIT SINGH                FORM 5"
200 PRINTTAB(0,23)CHR$130"************************************"
210 PRINTTAB(10,24)CHR$131"Key P for Page 1"
220 IF GET$="P" THEN CHAIN"PAGE1"
```

Figure 14.10   Computer program PRCOVER

PROGRAM — PAGE2

```
10 REM *** TRIG INVOLVED ***
20 MODE 1
30 MOVE 50,720:DRAW 400,720:DRAW 400,920:DRAW 50,720
40 PRINTTAB(1,10)"A":PRINTTAB(6,10)"c":PRINTTAB(12,10)"B"
50 PRINTTAB(12,2)"C":PRINTTAB(13,6)"a":PRINTTAB(6,5)"b"
60 COLOUR 2:PRINTTAB(3,0)"Page 2 - The trigonometry
   involved":COLOUR7
70 PRINTTAB(16,4)"Cosine angle A    = c/b"
80 PRINTTAB(16,6)"Sine angle A      = a/b"
90 PRINTTAB(16,8)"Tangent angle A   = a/c"
100 COLOUR 2:PRINTTAB(1,12)"In MODE 1 the VDU screen measures
    1280 divisions wide and 1024 divisions high."
110 PRINTTAB(1,14)"The screen is thus divided by a CO-ORDINATE
    grid giving values of X between 0 and 1279 horizontally"
120 PRINTTAB(0,17)"and of Y between 0 and 1023 vertically"
130 COLOUR 7:PRINTTAB(1,19)"In the triangle above, if A is
    at X,Y  then B is at X+c,Y.  The position of C  can be
    stated as being:"
140 COLOUR 2:PRINTTAB(5,23)"X+c+c*COS(A),Y+c*SIN(A)"
150 COLOUR 7: PRINTTAB(1,25)"NOTE: The BBC computer measures
    angles in Radians.  There are 2PI Radians in a circle.
    To convert Radians to degrees a term RAD is used."
160 COLOUR 2: PRINTTAB(20,28)"Hence the lines e.g."
170 COLOUR 2:PRINTTAB(5,30)"X+X1+R*COSRAD(I),Y+R*SINRAD(I)"
180 IF GET$="P"THEN CHAIN"LIST"
```

Figure 14.11   Computer program PAGE2

PROGRAM - DOGS

```
10 REM *** A PATTERN OF DOGS ***
20 MODE 7
30 PRINTTAB(9,0)CHR$131"A PATTERN OF DOGS"
40 PRINTTAB(1,4)"This program runs in MODE 7 which is     the 'Teletext' mode.
MODE 7 allows a    full    range of 16 colours, some of    which are 'flashing
colours"
50 PRINTTAB(2,10)CHR$131"The program produces a pattern of"
60 PRINTTAB(4,11)CHR$131"'dogs' in different colours"
70 PRINTTAB(2,14)CHR$134"Press any key to RUN the program"
80 PRINTTAB(6,16)CHR$134"Key P to return to LIST"
90 A$=GET$
100 IF A$="R" THEN GOTO120
110 IF A$="P" THEN CHAIN"LIST"
120 REPEAT:N=N+1
130 PRINTCHR$145CHR$234CHR$156CHR$156CHR$240CHR$156CHR$234CHR$146CHR$156CHR$156CHR$24
0CHR$147CHR$234CHR$156CHR$156CHR$240CHR$156CHR$234CHR$149CHR$234CHR$156CHR$240CHR$150CH
R$234CHR$156CHR$156CHR$240
140 PRINTCHR$145CHR$254CHR$255CHR$255CHR$163CHR$156CHR$254CHR$255CHR$255CHR$16
3CHR$147CHR$254CHR$255CHR$255CHR$163CHR$156CHR$254CHR$149CHR$254CHR$255CHR$163CHR$150CH
R$254CHR$255CHR$255CHR$163
150 PRINTCHR$145CHR$181CHR$156CHR$234CHR$156CHR$181CHR$156CHR$234CHR$14
7CHR$156CHR$181CHR$156CHR$234CHR$149CHR$156CHR$234CHR$181CHR$156CHR$234CHR$150CHR$156CH
R$181CHR$156CHR$234
160 PRINT
170 UNTIL N=6
```

Figure 14.12 Computer program DOGS

PROGRAM — PATTERN

```
10 REM *** A PATTERN ***
20 MODE 7
30 PRINTTAB(12,0)CHR$131"A PATTERN"
40 PRINTTAB(1,3)"This program runs a two-colour pattern."
50 PRINTTAB(1,4)"The pattern was built up from the use"
60 PRINTTAB(1,5)"of VDU 23,(240 to 255) drivers and"
70 PRINTTAB(1,6)"the REPEAT and NEXT commands. The"
80 PRINTTAB(1,7)"The pattern  uses pixel 'painting'"
90 PRINTTAB(2,12)CHR$134"Press any key to RUN the program"
100 PRINTTAB(6,14)CHR$134"Key P to return to LIST"
110 A$=GET$
120 IF A$="R" THEN GOTO 140
130 IF A$="P" THEN CHAIN"LIST"
140 MODE 5
150 REPEAT:Y=Y+2
160 FOR X=1 TO 19 STEP 1
170 VDU 23,240,24,24,24,255,255,24,24,24
180 VDU 23,241,24,36,66,129,129,66,36,24
190 COLOUR 1:PRINTTAB(X,Y)CHR$240
200 COLOUR 2:PRINTTAB(X,Y+1)CHR$241
210 NEXT X
220 UNTIL Y=28
```

Figure 14.13   Computer program PATTERN

A

NOTES ON MY COMPUTER PROJECT

by Ranjit Singh

The BBC computer can be programmed in any one of 8 MODES - MODES 0 to 7. MODES 1,2,5 and 7 are used in this project.

MODE 1 - medium resolution - 320 by 256. 4 colours - black, white, red, yellow. These 4 colours can be changed to any of the 16 available on the BBC computer by using VDU 19 drivers in the program.

MODE 2 - lower resolution - 160 by 256. All 16 colours.

MODE 5 - lower resolution - 160 by 256. 4 colours.

Mode 7 - the MODE in which the computer is set when first switched on. 'Teletext' type graphics can be produced in this MODE.

Note:- Most of the programs are set in MODE 1. These could have been set in MODE 0, which, with a resolution of 640 by 256, produces cleaner lines than MODE 1. However only 2 colours (black and white) are available in MODE 0.

PROGRAMMING PROCEDURES

The 3 flow charts, Figs 1, 2 and 3, show the procedures which were most often used in this project. These Procedures are the 2 BBC BASIC program loops:

```
FOR  -  NEXT   and   REPEAT  -  UNTIL

       and the PROCedure method

PROC  -  DEF PROC  -  ENDPROC
```

These program methods are fully shown in the programs included in the project sheets.

DRAWING LINES

The programs in this project which produce geometric outlines rely on the methods of co-ordinate geometry. The screen is divided up into a grid of tiny squares formed by 1280 vertical lines, numbered 0 to 1279 and 1024 horizontal lines numbered from 0 (at the bottom) to 1023. See Fig. 4.

Each of the vertical lines is given a value of X and each horizontal line is given a value of Y. The bottom left hand corner of the screen is X,Y =(0,0); the top right hand corner is (1279,1023). All other points on the screen can be referred to in terms of X,Y. In particular, the centre of the screen is (640,512).

In MODES 1,2 and 5 (also 4), the command MOVE X,Y places an invisible cursor at the point X,Y on the screen. The command DRAW X1,Y1 moves the cursor to the point X1,Y1 and, at the same time, draws a line as it moves. Thus the 3-line program:

Figure 14.14 Sheet A

B

```
5 MODE 1
10 MOVE 100,100
20 DRAW 900,100
RUN
```

will produce a horizontal line a little way up from the bottom of the screen. The 3-line program:

```
5 MODE 1
10 MOVE 900,100
20 DRAW 900,900
RUN
```

will produce a vertical line on the screen. The 5-line program:

```
5 MODE 1
10 MOVE 100,100
20 DRAW 900,100
30 DRAW 900,900
40 DRAW 100,100
RUN
```

will produce a right angle triangle. See Fig.4.

MODE 7 - TELETEXT PRINT AND GRAPHICS

Letters, figures and a variety of graphic shapes are obtained in MODE 7 by the use of the keyword CHR$ followed by chosen numbers. Note that when colours are used in MODE 7, every line must include its own colour keyword and number.

```
For ALL letters and numbers        For colour graphics

CHR$129 - Red              CHR$145 - red
CHR$130 - Green            CHR$146 - Green
CHR$131 - Yellow           CHR$147 - Yellow
CHR$132 - Blue             CHR$148 - Blue
CHR$133 - Magenta          CHR$149 - Magenta
CHR$134 - Cyan             CHR$150 - Cyan
CHR$135 - White            CHR$151 - White
CHR$141 - Double height
```

GRAPHIC SHAPES IN MODE 7

Groups of 6 squares, equal in overall size to the space taken up by a single letter, can be coloured to form shapes and patterns. See Fig.5. The shapes are arranged by adding together the values of the squares to be coloured, then adding 160 to the total. The keyword is again CHR$. Thus CHR$255 colours the whole of the 6-square rectangle - because:

$$1+4+8+16+160 = 189, \text{ giving } CHR\$189$$

If the shape is to be coloured (other than in white), then add the graphic colour code. Thus:

CHR$145CHR$189

produced the shape in a red colour.

Figure 14.15 Sheet B

D

```
        VDU 24,100;700;400;1000;

will form the graphics window shown in Fig.4.  Note the
semi-colons in the VDU 24 command.  To colour this window
red the command:
        GCOL 0,129

must follow the VDU 24 command.

            THE USE OF TAB

The command TAB, followed by X,Y co-ordinates places the
beginning of a line of print at the positions given by X,Y
according to the values shown in Fig.8 and 9.  Note that
the X,Y position (0,0) is the TOP left hand corner of the
screen for TAB commands.

            COLOURING SHAPES

In BBC BASIC programs, shapes other that graphic windows
can only be coloured as a series of triangles.  In order to
fill the triangles with colour, two corners of each triangle
must first be given followed by the command PLOT 85,X,Y
giving the co-ordinates of the third corner.  To colour the
triangle of Fig.4, line 30 of the program producing the
triangle must be changed to PLOT 85,900,900.  The complete
program becomes:

5 MODE 1
10 MOVE 100,100
20 DRAW 900,100
30 GCOL 0,1:PLOT 85,900,900
RUN

NOTE:  The GCOL 0,1 command asks for
red in graphics.
```

Figure 14.17 Sheet D

C

```
            'PIXEL' PAINTING

In MODES 0,1,2,4 and 5, patterns can be formed by
'pixel painting'.  Any of the 64 pixels in a square of 8 by 8
can be lit by using the VDU 'driver' VDU 23.
VDU 23 must be followed by 9 numbers, the first being any
CHR$ number between 240 and 255.  The remaining 8 numbers
form the pattern:

        VDU 23,240,a,b,c,d,e,f,g,h

in which a to h are numbers representing the addition of all
the squares in each line to be 'painted'.  The numbers in
each square in the lines are given in Fig.7.  Thus to
produce the shape coloured red in Fig.7:

            In line a  -  16+8  = 24
            In line b  -  32+4  = 36
            In line c  -  64+2  = 66
            In line d  -  128+1 = 129

and so on.  This gives a program line:

        VDU23,240,24,36,66,129,129,66,36,24

which must be followed by;

        COLOUR 1:PRINT CHR$240

to produce the required coloured pattern of pixels.  In this
example the colour is red.

        TEXT AND GRAPHICS 'WINDOWS'

When it is necessary to restrict text to a 'window' on the
screen, the VDU 'driver' VDU 28 is used.  In MODE 1, the
size of the window is governd by X,Y co-ordinates as in
Fig.9.  The full command to form a window is:

        VDU 28,a,b,c,d

in which a is the X co-ordinate of the left hand edge of the
window; b is the Y co-ordinate of the bottom; c is the X
co-ordinate of the right hand edge; d Is the Y co-ordinate
of the top edge.  Thus the VDU line:

        VDU 28,1,3,38,1

produces the text window shown in Fig.9.  Note the commas in
the VDU 28 command.

To produce a window in which graphics only can be
displayed, VDU 24 is used.  With the VDU 24 command the X,Y
co-ordinates as in Fig.4 must be used.  Thus:
```

Figure 14.16 Sheet C

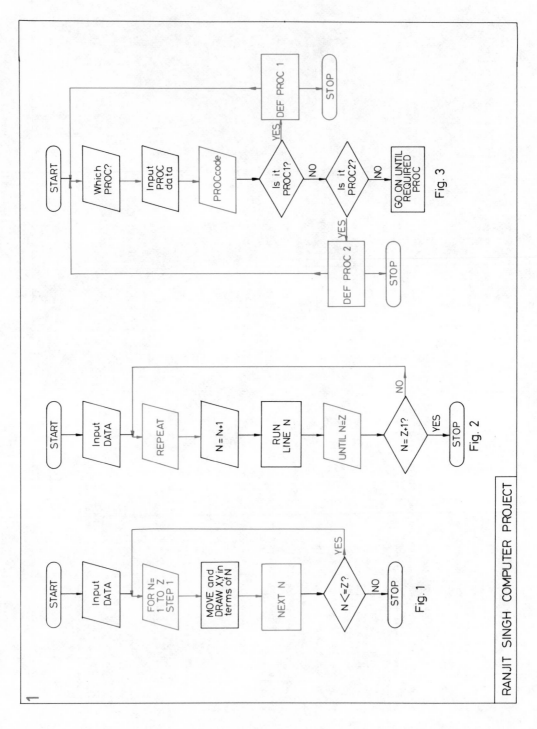

Figure 14.18 Sheet 1

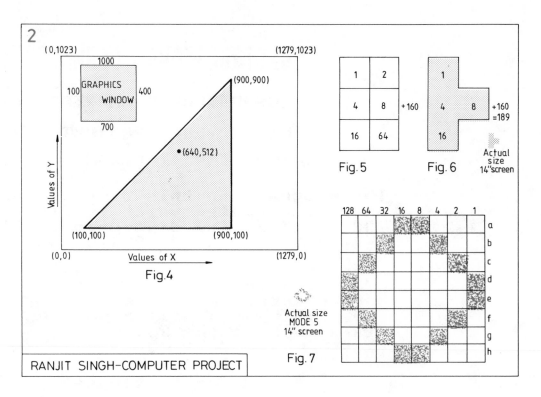

Figure 14.19 Sheet 2

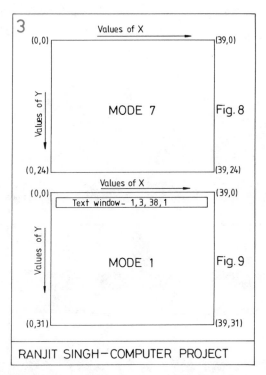

Figure 14.20 Sheet 3

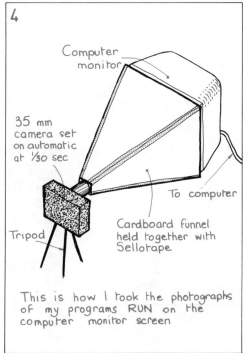

Figure 14.21 Sheet 4

CONSTRUCTIONAL GEOMETRY

GCSE: GRAPHICAL COMMUNICATION

FIFTH YEAR -PROJECT

by RANJIT SINGH

The programs on this disc can be run on any BBC computer which is fitted with a 133 mm (5.25 in) disc drive. All the programs are in BBC BASIC language

The programs allow you to show on the VDU of a computer a variety of geometrical shapes and forms as shown on the LIST which will appear on the VDU if you press the key P

Key P for next page

Figure 14.22 Printout of screen from program PRCOVER

Figure 14.23 Printout of screen from program HOUSE

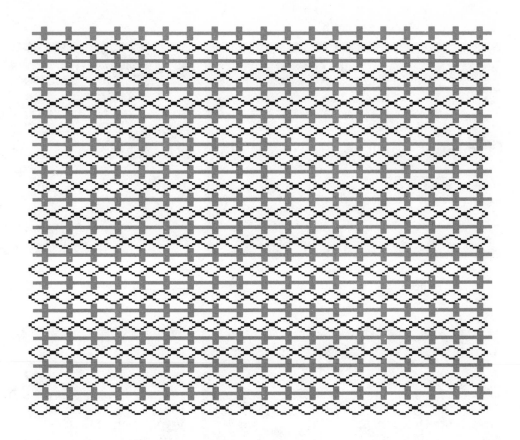

Figure 14.24 Printout of screen from program PATTERN

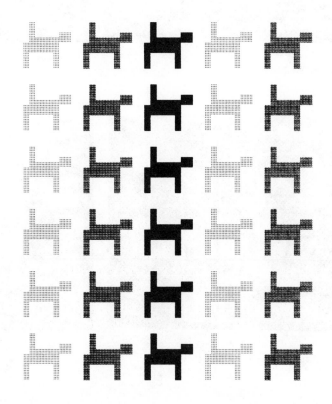

Figure 14.25 Printout of screen from program DOGS

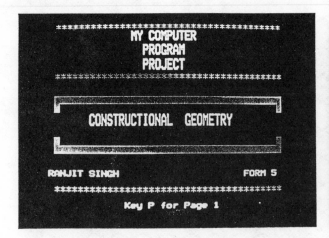

Figure 14.26   Screen — PRCOVER

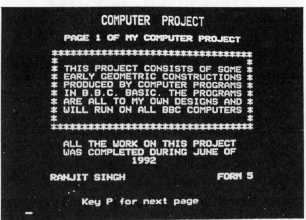

Figure 14.27   Screen — PAGE1

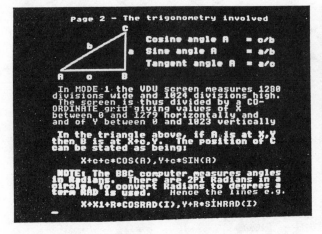

Figure 14.28   Screen — PAGE2

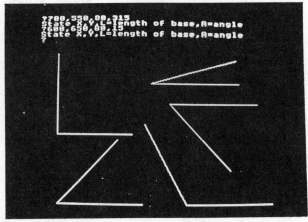

Figure 14.29   Screen — ANGLES

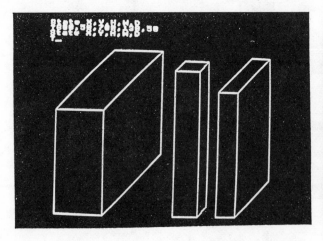

Figure 14.30   Screen — OBLIQUE

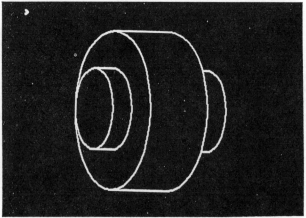

Figure 14.31   Screen — SPINDLE

214

14.6 Carrier Bag Project

This project is an example of a graphic project produced by a pupil in a school in answer to a stated *design brief*. It is a typical *mini-project*, set as a work task covering a period of half a term. It is also an example of one which requires that a model of the final design solution be produced. In this example, the model was made from paper. Both sides of the model carry the graphic design, which formed a major part of the project.

This mini-project could form half of a full project for examination purposes for presentation to a moderator. All the sheets from the project have been printed on the following pages. The complete project consists of:

Notes 1 and 2 — Figs 14.32 and 14.33 — preliminary rough notes, with sketches, forming the basis for Drawing Sheets 1 to 4.

Sheets 1 to 4 — Figs 14.34 to 14.37 — show ideas for solutions and a chosen solution from the ideas.

Sheet 5 — Fig. 14.38 — includes a First Angle dimensioned drawing and a surface development of a pattern for the bag.

Model — a photograph of the model of the chosen design is included — Fig. 14.39. The actual model would, of course, be submitted for moderation. A variety of graphic techniques and methods have been used in the sheets of drawings for this project:

Notes written in black and red biro pens
Freehand drawings coloured with colour pencils
Freehand front views coloured with colour pencils
Front view drawings with coloured ink lines
Water colour wash
First Angle projection
Surface development
A model

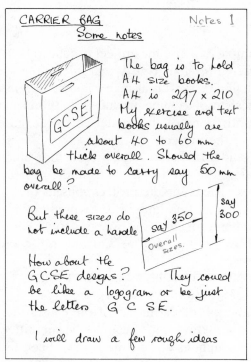

Figure 14.32 Note 1 Carrier bag project

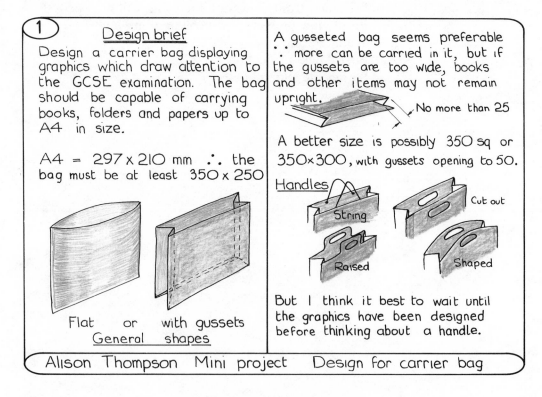

Figure 14.33 Note 2 Carrier bag project

Figure 14.34 Ideas for solutions 1

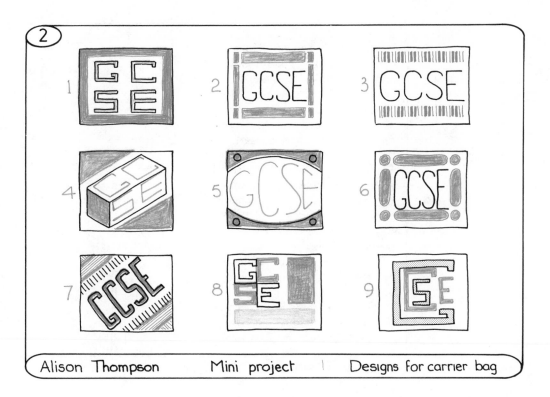

Figure 14.35 Ideas for solutions 2

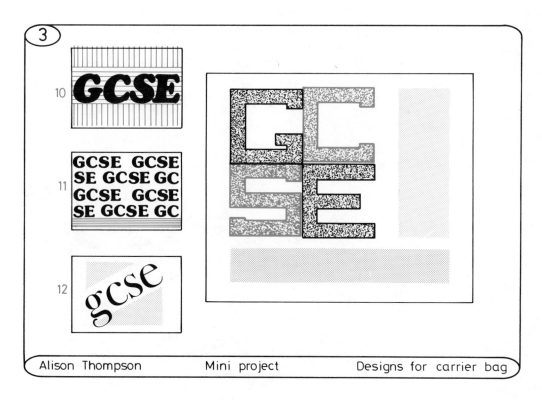

Figure 14.36 Ideas for solutions 3

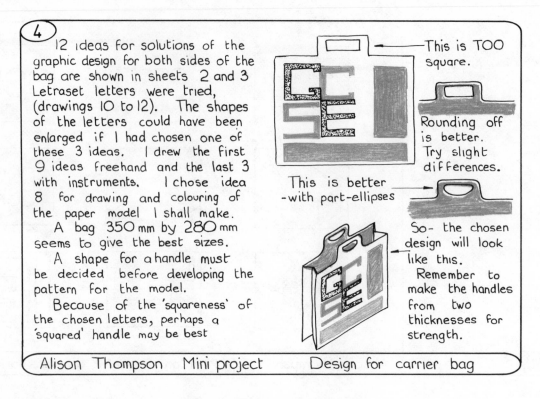

4

12 ideas for solutions of the graphic design for both sides of the bag are shown in sheets 2 and 3 Letraset letters were tried, (drawings 10 to 12). The shapes of the letters could have been enlarged if I had chosen one of these 3 ideas. I drew the first 9 ideas freehand and the last 3 with instruments. I chose idea 8 for drawing and colouring of the paper model I shall make.

A bag 350mm by 280mm seems to give the best sizes.

A shape for a handle must be decided before developing the pattern for the model.

Because of the 'squareness' of the chosen letters, perhaps a 'squared' handle may be best

This is TOO square.

Rounding off is better. Try slight differences.

This is better -with part-ellipses

So- the chosen design will look like this.

Remember to make the handles from two thicknesses for strength.

Alison Thompson   Mini project   Design for carrier bag

Figure 14.37   Ideas for solutions 4

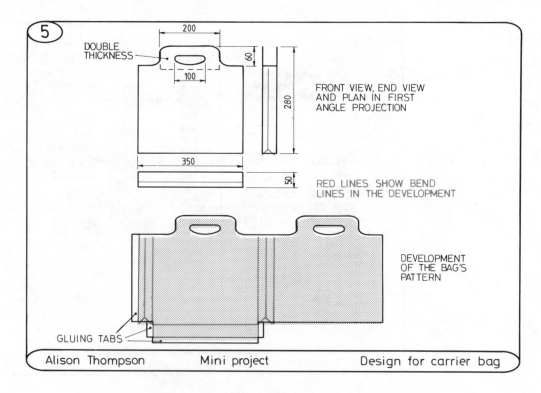

5

DOUBLE THICKNESS

200

60

100

350

280

50

FRONT VIEW, END VIEW AND PLAN IN FIRST ANGLE PROJECTION

RED LINES SHOW BEND LINES IN THE DEVELOPMENT

DEVELOPMENT OF THE BAG'S PATTERN

GLUING TABS

Alison Thompson   Mini project   Design for carrier bag

Figure 14.38   Chosen design solution — Carrier bag

218

Figure 14.39 Model for carrier bag

14.7 Building Drawing Project

This graphic project, consisting of a series of sheets of drawings contained in a folder, were designed and drawn by a 16-year-old schoolgirl. The details in the project relate to the bungalow where she lives with her family. Some of the graphics involved were designed from information given in maps and documents found in the title deeds of the bungalow, but most of the information was obtained by observation, by taking measurements and from notes taken around the bungalow and its garden. Nine of the sheets of drawings are shown on pages 222 to 226. The sheets of drawings were contained in a folder made from stiff cardboard. Details of the basis for a design for the cover of the folder, together with a copy of the finished design are shown in Figs 14.40 and 14.41. The completed cover design was produced with the aid of Letraset dry transfer lettering. A complete list of the drawings for the project is given below. Nine of the fourteen sheets are reproduced here in this book.

Sheet 1 — Fig. 14.42 — eight of the freehand drawings from which the final sheets of drawings numbered 1 to 8 were produced. The rough pencil sketches leading up to these freehand drawings are not shown here. They were however included in the final project.

Drawing 1 — Fig. 14.43 — a map, drawn to a scale of 1:10 000 from an Ordnance Survey map of the district in which the girl lives. Field 179, in which Farm Close was built, is outlined in red.

Drawing 2 — Fig. 14.44 — a site location plan, drawn scale 1:1000 with instruments. The outline of Plot 2, where the bungalow was built, has been outlined in red.

Drawing 3 — Fig. 14.45 — a site plan, scale 1:200 of number 2 Farm Close, with some details emphasised in red.

Drawing 4 — Fig. 14.46 — a scale 1:50 building plan of the bungalow, with details of the position and sizes of its rooms. The bathroom and kitchen have been colour washed to draw attention to the fact that they are again shown on a larger scale in Drawing 5.

Drawing 5 — Fig. 14.47 — a scale 1:10 plan of the bathroom and kitchen showing the positions of various fittings. The fittings have been colour washed.

Drawing 6 — Fig. 14.48 — a two-point estimated perspective of the bungalow, with parts colour shaded with colour pencils. The human figures and trees were added from dry transfer sheets in the Letraset Architectural range.

Drawing 7 — Fig. 14.49 — two-point estimated perspective drawing of the sitting room with parts coloured with colour pencils.

Drawing 8 — Fig. 14.50 — a communications chart drawn to an approximate scale of 10 mm represents 5 km. Colour has been added to emphasise selected details.

Not shown here:

Sheet 9 — A planometric drawing of details of doors and windows in (a) the entrance hall and (b) a bedroom.

Sheet 10 — Drawings giving details of the construction of features, such as: roof, door lining, window sills, double glazing.

Sheet 11 — A series of graphs and charts. Details of the population trends, numbers of houses built over the years, relationship between the decline of farming in the area and other forms of employment, different forms of transport in the district over the years.

Sheet 12 — Photographs of the bungalow and its surroundings, mounted on card.

Sheet 13 — An Index of the sheets of drawing.

Figure 14.40 Building project — cover

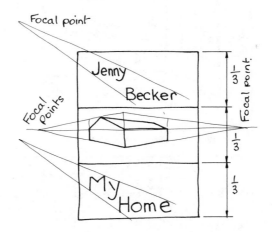

Figure 14.41 Cover design principles

Drawing 1 - Freehand map of the area showing position of field in which my house was built. From 1:25,000 O.S. map and enlarged to scale 1:10,000

2. Site location plan, scale 1:1000 of position of 2 Farm Close

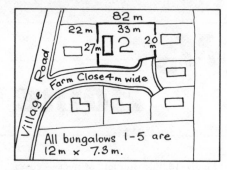

3. Site plan of 2 Farm Close drawn to scale 1:200

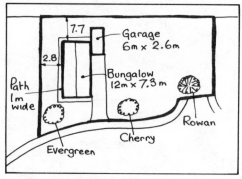

4. Building plan - Scale 1:50

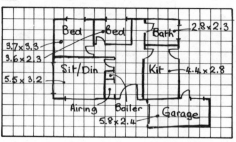

5. Plan of kitchen and bathroom - Scale 1:10

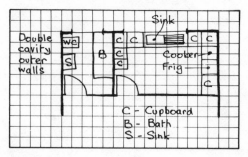

C - Cupboard
B - Bath
S - Sink

6. Two-point estimated perspective of bungalow

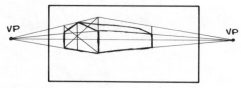

7. Two-point estimated perspective of two walls of sitting/dining room

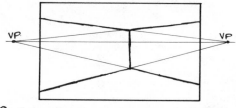

8. Communications - approx scale-1cm=5km

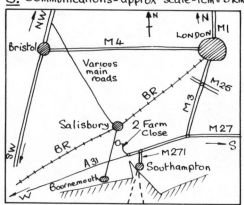

Figure 14.42 Building project — Sheet 1

Figure 14.43 Drawing 1

Figure 14.44 Drawing 2

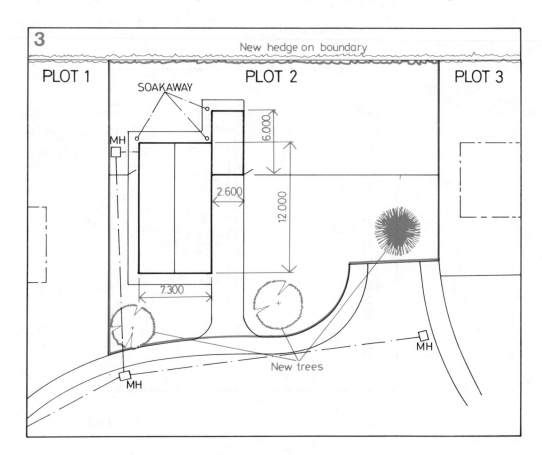

Figure 14.45 Drawing 3

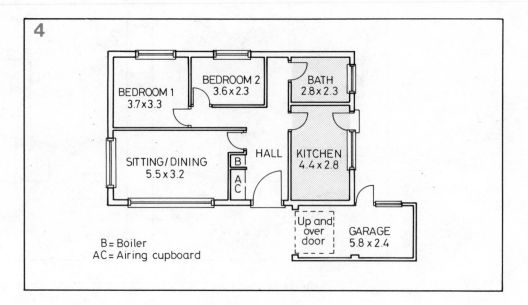

Figure 14.46 Drawing 4

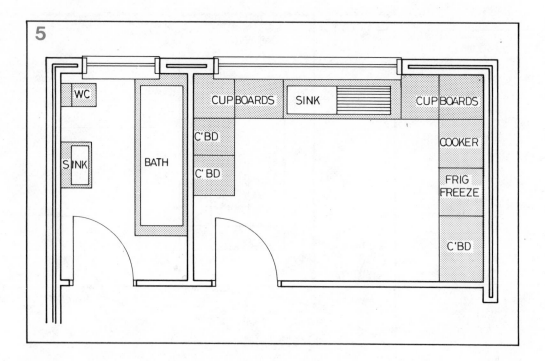

Figure 14.47 Drawing 5

Figure 14.48 Drawing 6

Figure 14.49 Drawing 7

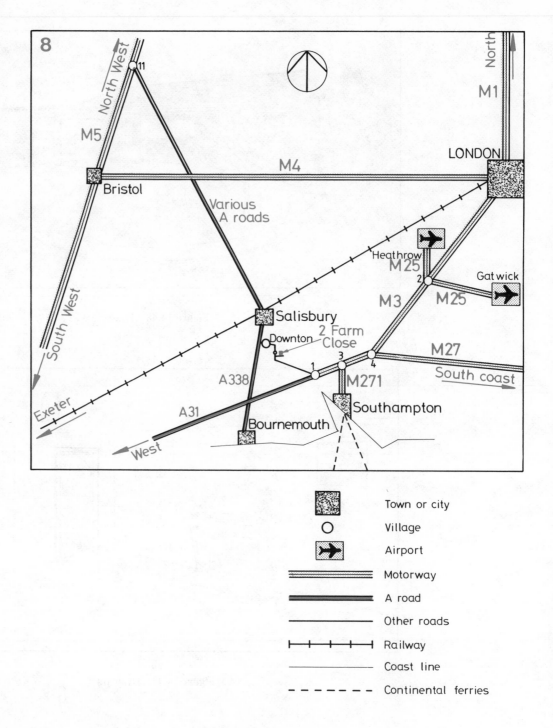

Figure 14.50 Drawing 8

15 Solutions to Exercises

Worked Example 2.1

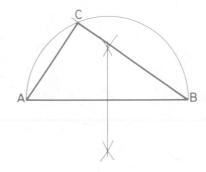

Figure 15.1   Solution 2.1

Worked Example 2.2

    (a) **B**
    (b) **D**
    (c) **C**
    (d) **A**
    (e) Segment
    (f) Sector
    (g) Quadrant
    (h) Sector

Exercise 2.3

    (a) Major axis; minor axis
    (b) and (c) Fig. 15.2

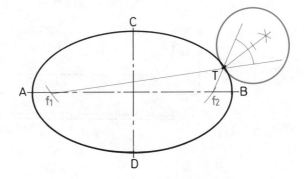

Figure 15.2   Solution 2.3

Exercise 2.4

$A = 13 \text{ cm} \times 9 \text{ cm} = 117 \text{ cm}^2$

$B = (9 \text{ cm} \times 9 \text{ cm})/2 = 40.5 \text{ cm}^2$

$C = (15 \text{ cm} + 10 \text{ cm})/2 \times 9 \text{ cm} = 112.5 \text{ cm}^2$

$D = (4 \text{ cm} \times 5 \text{ cm})/2 \times 5 = 50 \text{ cm}^2$

$E = (14 \times 6.5) + (3.14 \times 7^2)/2 - (3.14 \times 4.5^2) = 104.345 \text{ cm}^2$

$F = $ Fig. 15.3

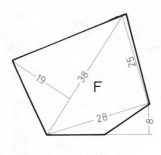

361 + 350 + 60
Area F = 771 sq mm

Figure 15.3 Solution 2.4

Exercise 2.5

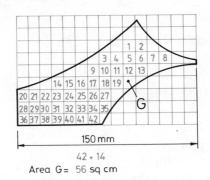

150 mm

42 + 14
Area G = 56 sq cm

Figure 15.4 Solution 2.5

Exercise 2.6

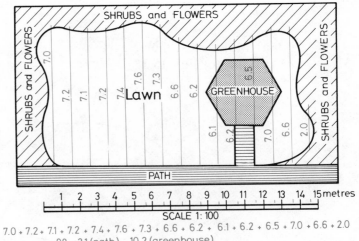

7.0 + 7.2 + 7.1 + 7.2 + 7.4 + 7.6 + 7.3 + 6.6 + 6.2 + 6.1 + 6.2 + 6.5 + 7.0 + 6.6 + 2.0
= 98 − 2.1 (path) − 10.2 (greenhouse)

Area = 85.7 sq metres

Figure 15.5 Solution 2.6

228

Exercise 2.7

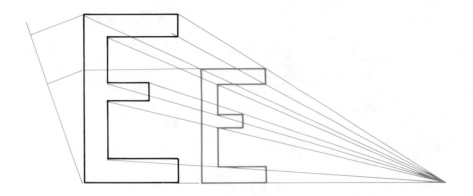

Figure 15.6   Solution 2.7

Exercise 2.8

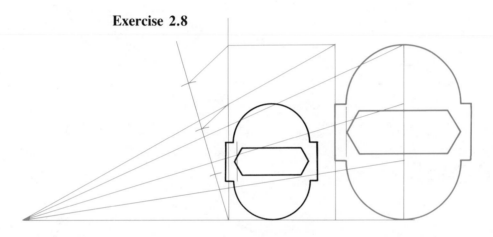

Figure 15.7   Solution 2.8

Exercise 2.9

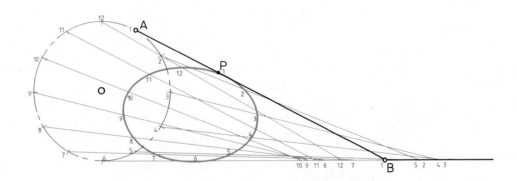

Figure 15.8   Solution 2.9

Exercise 2.10

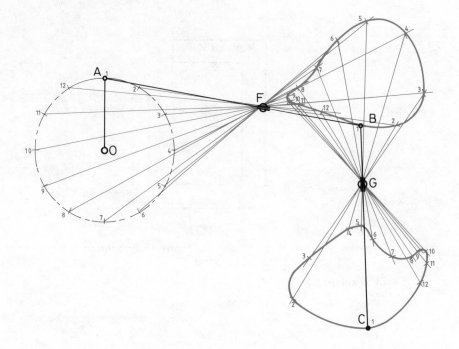

Figure 15.9 Solution 2.10

Exercise 2.11

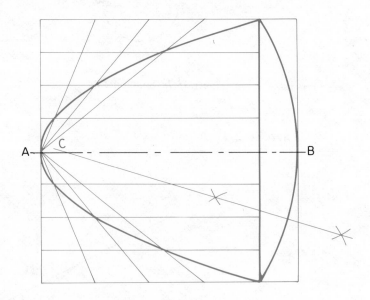

Figure 15.10 Solution 2.11

Exercise 2.12

Note: This solution has been worked with the aid of a trammel.

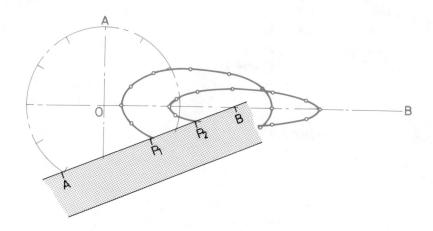

Figure 15.11 Solution 2.12

Exercise 2.13

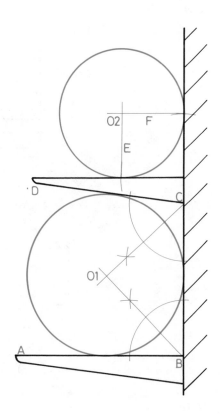

Figure 15.12 Solution 2.13

To construct the centre for the circle **B**, bisect the two angles **ABC** and **BCD**. The centre **01** is where the two bisectors cross.

To construct the centre for circle **A**, draw lines **E** and **F** parallel and 35 mm distant from the wall line and the top of the shelf line. The required centre **02** is where the two parallels cross.

231

Exercises 3.1 to 3.6

3.1 — D
3.2 — C
3.3 — B
3.4 — F
3.5 — C and **D**
3.6 — A

Exercise 3.7

(a) **G** — 2, 3 and 4
  H — 3, 5 and 6
(b) **A** — 7, 10 and 12
  B — 7, 8 and 12
  C — 7, 8, 9 and 11

Exercise 3.8

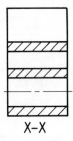

X–X

Figure 15.13 Solution 3.8

Exercise 3.9

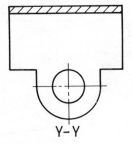

Y–Y

Figure 15.14 Solution 3.9

Exercise 3.10

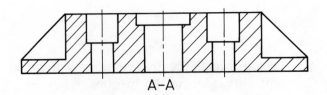

A–A

Figure 15.15 Solution 3.10

Exercise 3.11

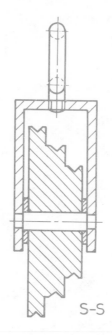

Figure 15.16 Solution 3.11

S-S

Exercise 4.1

    (a) A circle
    (b) An ellipse
    (c) A regular hexagonal pyramid
    (d) A truncated octagonal pyramid
    (e) First Angle
    (f) Third Angle orthographic projection
    (g) **B**
    (h) **C**

Exercise 4.2

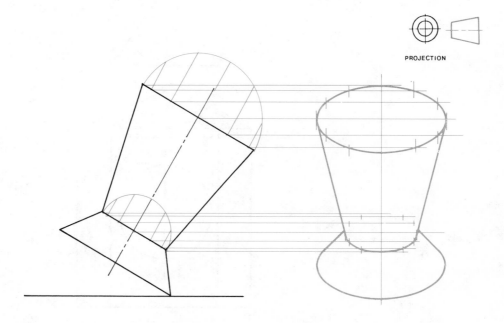

PROJECTION

Figure 15.17 Solution 4.2

Exercise 4.3

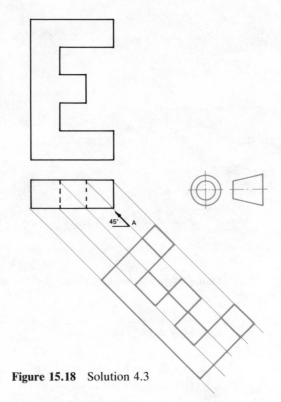

Figure 15.18   Solution 4.3

Exercise 4.4

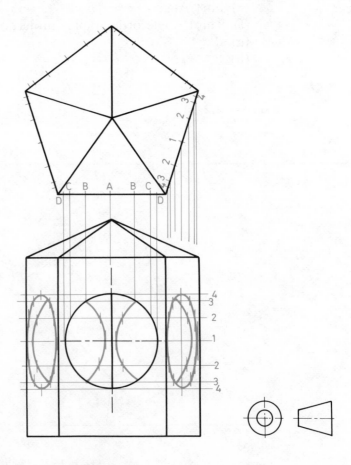

Figure 15.19   Solution 4.4

Points on the required ellipses and part ellipses were found by:

1. Draw horizontal lines **1, 2, 3** and **4**.
2. Where these lines meet the given circle project up to the given plan, giving points **A, B, C** and **D**.
3. Transfer points **A** to **D** on to each side of the plan pentagon.
4. Project from each pentagon side back to the front view.
5. Where these projection lines meet lines **1, 2, 3** and **4** are points on the ellipses.

Exercise 4.5

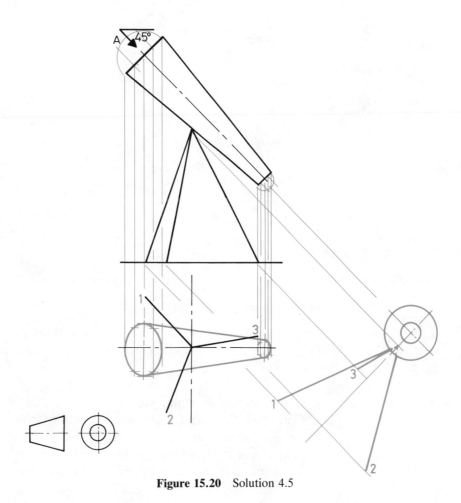

Figure 15.20 Solution 4.5

The construction lines for plotting points on the required ellipses are shown in red. The positions of the bottoms of the three tripod legs in the auxiliary plan — points **1, 2** and **3**, have been found by measuring the distance of points from the centre line in the plan view and transferring the measurements by compass to the correct side of the centre line in the auxiliary plan.

Exercise 4.6

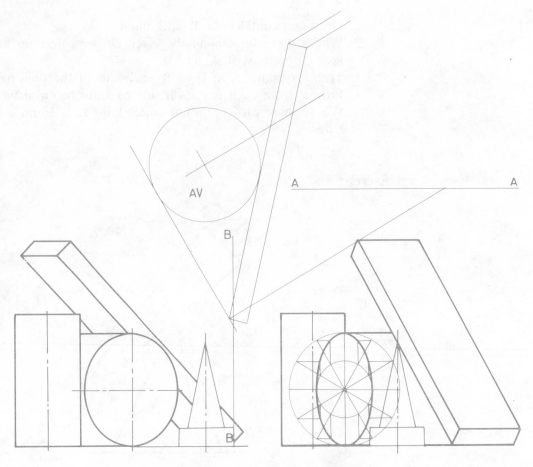

Figure 15.21 Solution 4.6

Note the similarity between this Example and Worked Example 4.12 (page 63). However, the solution has been worked in a slightly different manner.

The order of working was:

1. Construct the auxiliary view **AV**.
2. Construct the front view by projection from the plan, with vertical measurements taken either from the given pictorial drawings or by measurements from the auxiliary view **AV**.
3. Construct the end view by projecting from the front view and by taking measurements above line **AA** and transferring them to right and left of line **BB** in the end view.

After finding the axes by construction, the two ellipses were constructed using the auxiliary circles method.

Exercise 5.1

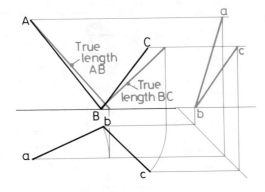

Figure 15.22   Solution 5.1

To draw the end view refer to Section 2.
   To find the true length refer to Section 5.1.

Exercise 5.2

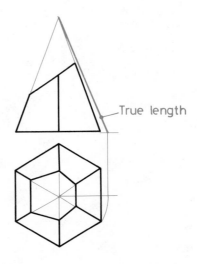

Figure 15.23   Solution 5.2

To find the required true length see Worked Example 5.1.

Exercise 5.3

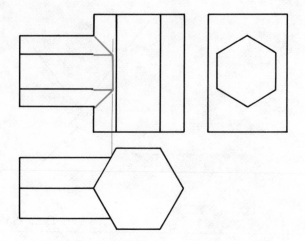

Figure 15.24 Solution 5.3

Project as shown by the lines in red.

Note: In all the given examples of curves of intersection, the axes of the intersecting solids have been in the same plane. The construction of curves of intersections of solids whose axes meet in two planes is not required at GCSE level.

Exercise 5.4

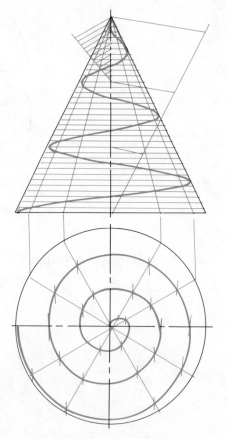

Figure 15.25 Solution 5.4

1. Divide the height of the cone into 3 equal parts.
2. Divide each of these pitch lengths into 12 equal parts.
3. Divide the plan circle into 12 equal parts.
4. Join these 12 points to the apex in the plan.
5. Project these sloping lines into the front view.
6. Complete the 3 pitches of the helices.
7. The plan of the helices can now be projected.

Exercise 5.5

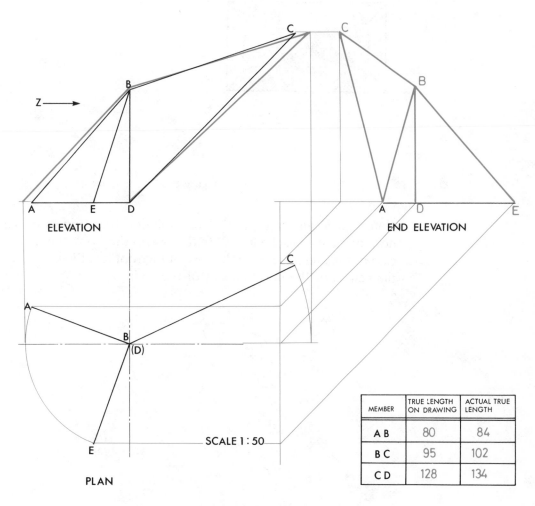

MEMBER	TRUE LENGTH ON DRAWING	ACTUAL TRUE LENGTH
A B	80	84
B C	95	102
C D	128	134

Figure 15.26 Solution 5.5

1. Projections from the given elevation and plan into the required end elevation were made via line LM and 45° lines.
2. The required true lengths were constructed by drawing arcs on to the horizontal centre line through B in the plan and then projecting into the given elevation.

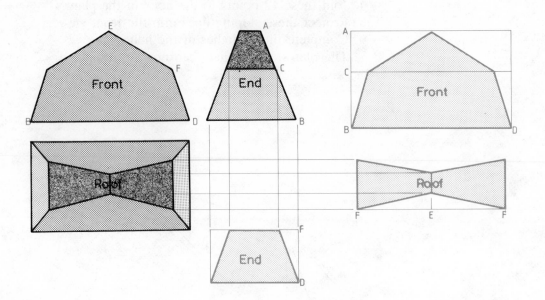

Figure 15.27 Solution 6.1

Note that in all three parts of this solution **true lengths** of part of each of the developments must be found. In the case of the front, this is the length **AB**; in the case of the end it is **DF**; in the case of the roof it is **EF** each side of a line through the centre of the development of the roof.

Exercise 6.2

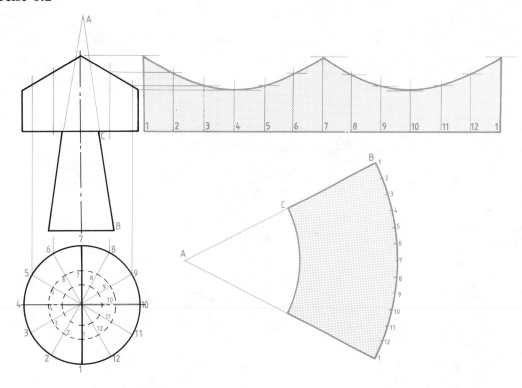

Figure 15.28 Solution 6.2

1. Divide the plan circle of the upper part of the model into 12 equal parts.
2. Draw a line level with the base of the front view of the upper part.
3. Measure off with a compass 12 of the divisions on the plan circle.
4. Draw verticals at these points — 1 to 12 to 1.
5. Project the points 1 to 12 in the plan into the front view.
6. Where these lines cross the sloping edge of the front view project horizontally on to the 12 verticals on the development.
7. Draw a curve through the plot points so obtained.
8. Find the point **A**, the apex of the cone of the lower part of the model.
9. Construct the development of the part cone on an arc of radius **AB**, with radius **AC** for the top edge of the development.
10. See Section 6.5 for completing the development.

Exercise 6.3

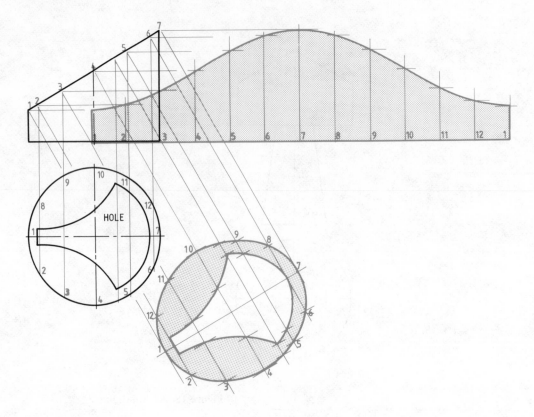

Figure 15.29   Solution 6.3

This solution follows closely on the two Worked Examples 6.1 and 6.7.

   Note how the 12 equal divisions of the plan circle are projected from the plan, to the front view, then to the development of the upright part of the cylinder and to the true shape of the upper surface.

Exercise 6.4

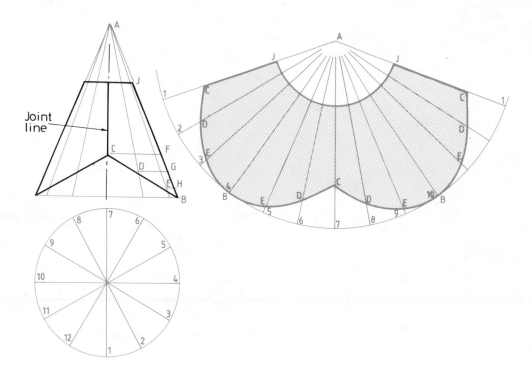

Figure 15.30 Solution 6.4

1. Draw lines on the front view of the complete cone.
2. Draw the plan circle of the complete cone.
3. Divide this circle into 12 equal parts.
4. Join the 12 points to the apex **A** in both plan and front view.
5. Construct a development of the complete cone. Section 6.5.
6. Draw **CF, DG** and **EH** parallel to the base of the front view.
7. Set a compass to **AF, AG** and **AH** in turn and from **A** in the development strike arcs along the appropriate lines to obtain the points **C, D** and **E**.
8. Set a compass to **AJ** and draw the arc of the top of the development.
9. Complete the development as shown.

Exercise 6.5

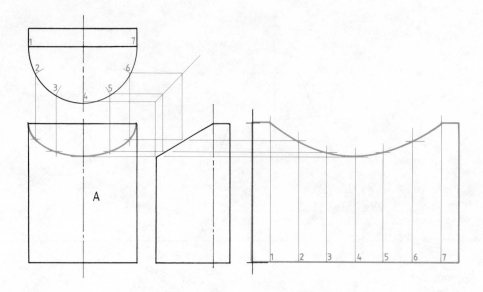

Figure 15.31 Solution 6.5

The curve to complete the front view was obtained by projecting from the given plan and end view via a 45° line.

To find the development follow the construction method given in Section 6.4.

Exercise 6.6

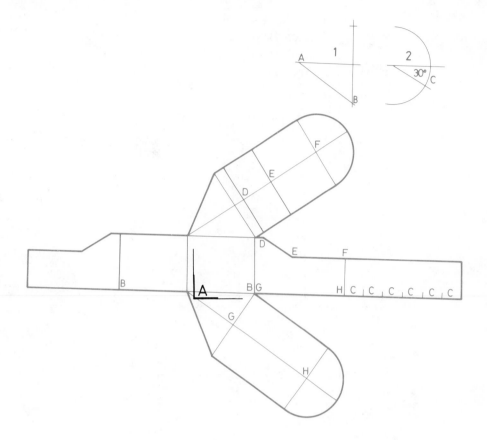

Figure 15.32 Solution 6.6

In this Exercise in order to make sure that true lengths are constructed:

AB in development   = AB in construction 1
C   in development   = C   in construction 2
DE in development of top = DE in development of side
EF in development of top = EF in development of side
GH in development of base = GH in development of side

Exercise 7.1

(a) Circle A — red
Area B — orange
Area C — pink
Area D — blue
Area E/F — yellow/purple
Area G — mauve
(b) Fig. 15.33
(c) Fig. 15.34

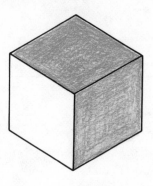

Figure 15.33 Solution 7.1(b)

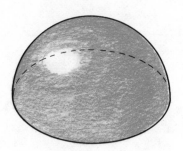

Figure 15.34 Solution 7.1(c)

Exercise 7.2

(a) Fig. 15.35
(b) Fig. 15.36
(iv) A 2-point perspective drawing

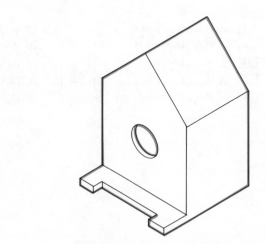

Figure 15.35 Solution 7.2(a)

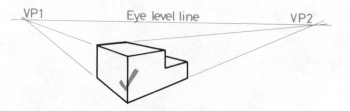

Figure 15.36 Solution 7.2(b)

Exercise 8.1

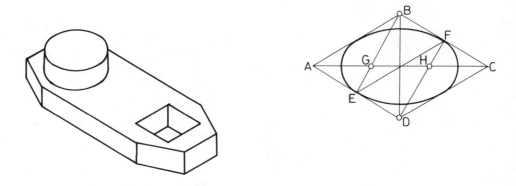

Figure 15.37 Solution 8.1

Exercise 8.1 stated that the 4-centre compass arcs methods could be used. This is a geometrical method of drawing isometric ellipses. Note that this construction does not result in accurate ellipses, but is an acceptable method when dealing with isometric circles of less than about 50 mm in diameter. The drawing Fig. 15.37 shows the method:

1. Draw the isometric 'square' ABCD.
2. Draw its diagonals AC and BD.
3. Draw EF to find the centre of the 'square'.
4. Draw BE and DF to obtain G and H.
5. The 4 centres are at **B, D, G** and **H**.

Exercise 8.2

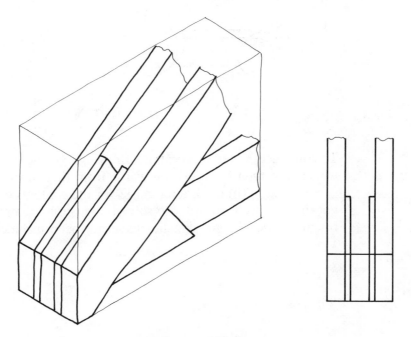

Figure 15.38 Solution 8.2

An 'isometric' box was first drawn in light construction lines. The required freehand isometric drawing was then constructed inside the 'box'.

Exercise 8.3

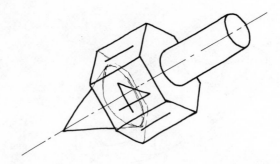

Figure 15.39 Solution 8.3

The Exercise left the choice of whether one is to look at the top or from underneath the spinner. This solution is the one looking down from above.

Exercise 8.4

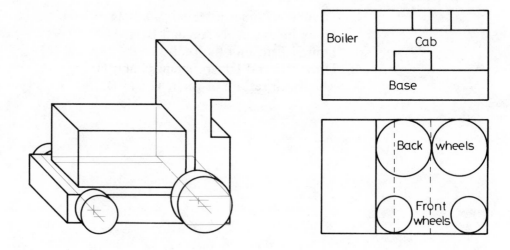

Figure 15.40 Solution 8.4

To construct the required cabinet drawing, commence by drawing the base. The wheels can then be drawn outwards from their position attached to the base.

Note that in (b) the Exercise asks for the contents of the box to be drawn and not the box itself. In order to solve (b) several attempts were made freehand in rough. These 'design' sketches have not been included in the given solution.

Exercise 8.5

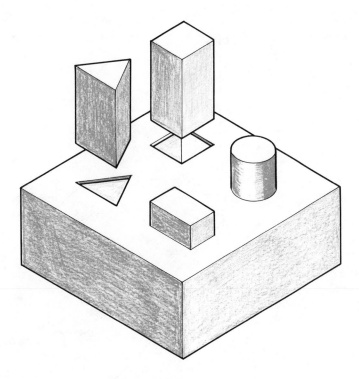

Figure 15.41 Solution 8.5

Colour was added to this solution with colour pencils to give a 3-D appearance to the drawing. In examination conditions, colour is possibly best added with colour pencils. The pencils are easy to take into an examination room, do not require water, and are clean to use, unlike some other colouring media which require special conditions if they are to be applied without difficulty.

Exercise 8.6

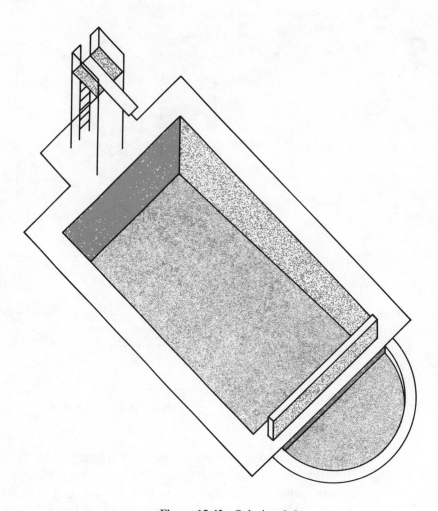

Figure 15.42 Solution 8.6

Three shades of colour were added to this drawing to give a 3-D appearance. The colour was added by brush, using water colour paints. Not really advisable under examination conditions, but suitable for use elsewhere.

Exercise 8.7

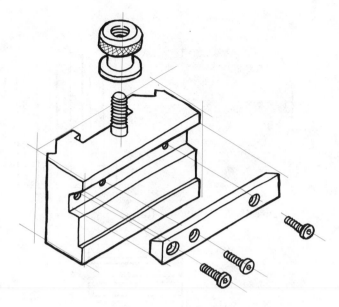

Figure 15.43 Solution 8.7

Always commence exploded freehand drawing with fine construction lines forming a 'box' within which the main part of the drawing can be constructed. Then draw further fine construction lines along the centres of the 'exploded' parts.

Exercise 8.8

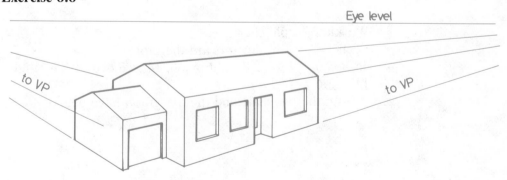

Figure 15.44 Solution 8.8

Note that the outline only of the bungalow sketch has been drawn. There would be insufficient time during an examination to produce a more complete drawing.

    (a) The lounge and dining area

    (b) Either — back door or pathways

Exercise 9.1

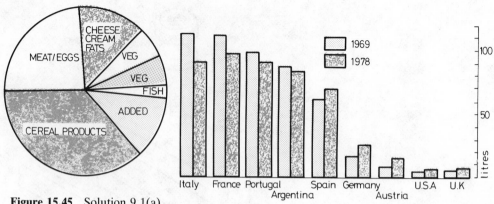

Figure 15.45 Solution 9.1(a)

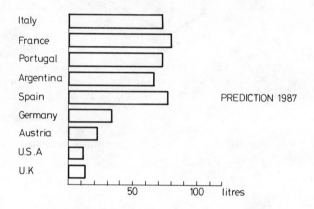

PREDICTION 1987

Figure 15.46 Solution 9.1(b)

Working for pie chart:

Each 1% = 3.6°. Sectors are therefore:

$36 \times 3.6 = 130°; 24 \times 3.6 = 86; 14 \times 3.6 = 50°; 6 \times 3.6 = 21°; 2 \times 3.6 = 7°;$
$12 \times 3.6 = 44°.$

Both the pie chart and the bar graph have been colour shaded.

Exercise 10.1

a — A Bearing;

b — A spring;

c — A screw thread — external;

d — External;

e — Pitch; circle; diameter;

f — Radius;

g — Number;

Exercise 10.2

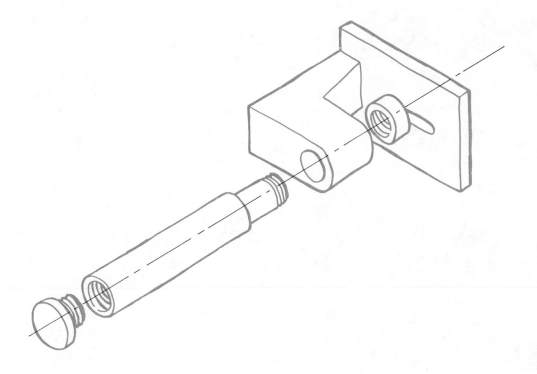

Figure 15.47   Solution 10.2

Exercise 10.3

(a) SQUARE ON SHAFT   —   1
     FLANGE   —   9
     HEXAGONAL NUT   —   4
     BOSS   —   7
     DRILLED HOLE   —   2
     COUNTER BORE   —   3
     CHAMFER   — 11
     UNDERCUT   —   6
     EXTERNAL SCREW THREAD —   5
     FILLET RADIUS   — 10

(b) Fig. 15.48

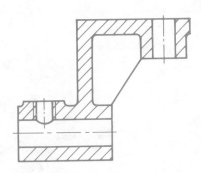

Figure 15.48   Solution 10.3(b)

Exercise 11.1

Fig. 15.49

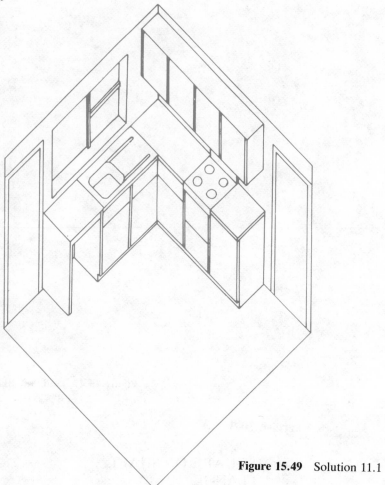

Figure 15.49 Solution 11.1

Exercise 11.2

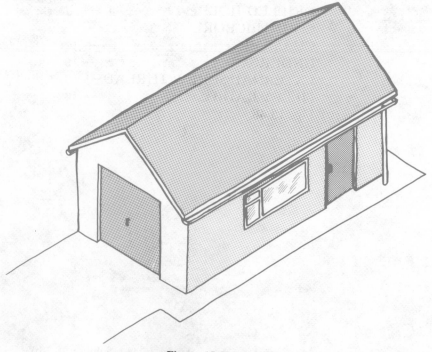

Figure 15.50 Solution 11.2(a)

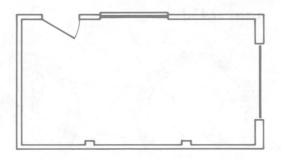

Figure 15.51 Solution 11.2(b)

(a) Fig. 15.50. Three shades of colour have been added to the drawing for this solution.
(b) Fig. 15.51. Note that if a plan of a building such as this garage is asked for, it usually means a plan without the roof in position.

Exercise 11.3

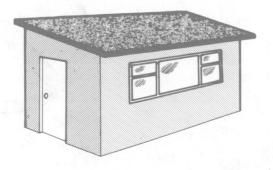

Figure 15.52 Solution 11.3(a)

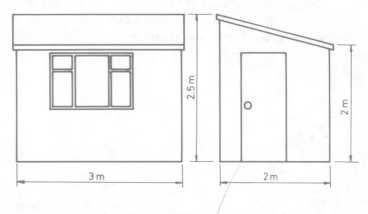

Figure 15.53 Solution 11.3(b)

(a) Fig. 15.52
(b) Fig. 15.53

Exercise 12.1

Figure 15.54 Solution 12.1

Five design sketches were drawn, all based on a similar theme — the idea of shoes, shoe marks and boot marks. A variety of shadings were added to these design sketches. The idea chosen as a solution to the design brief shows a pair of shoes with a bar across them.

Exercise 12.2

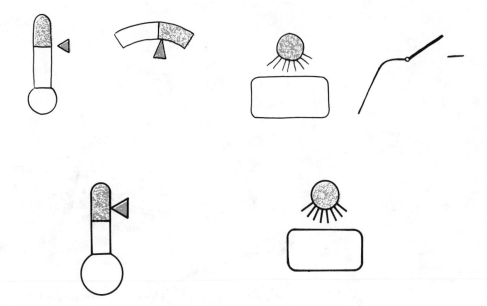

Figure 15.55   Solution 12.2

Use of colour in this solution adds to the meaning of the symbols chosen to represent the engine heating and the sun-roof open designs.

Exercise 12.3

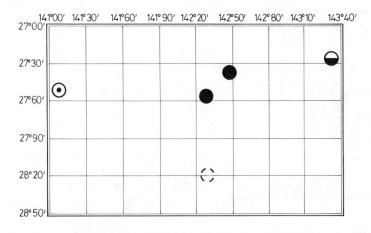

Figure 15.56   Solution 12.2

A mapping exercise which requires care in its solution.

Exercise 12.4

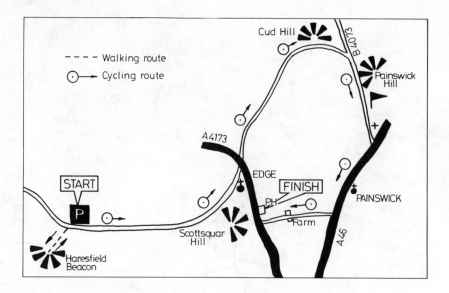

Figure 15.57 Solution 12.4

Another map exercise. There is insufficient time in an examination to answer this type of question except by working most of the solution freehand.

Exercise 13.1

Exercise 13.2

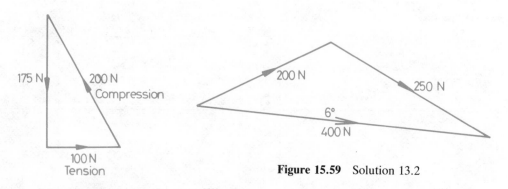

Figure 15.58 Solution 13.1

Figure 15.59 Solution 13.2

Note in the solution 13.2, the direction of action of the resultant of 400 N is against the direction of action of the other two forces in the triangle. This is because the 400 N force is intended to replace the other two forces. This triangle of forces does not show 3 forces in equilibrium.

Exercise 13.3

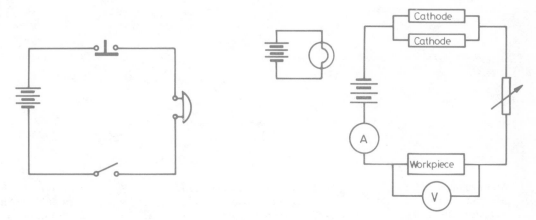

Figure 15.60 Solution 13.3   **Figure 15.61** Solution 13.4

Exercise 13.4

Both of these solutions require some knowledge of simple electric circuits. Note that in the symbol for a battery, the longer of the two lines for each cell denotes the **positive** connection of the battery.

Index